SERVICING ELECTRONIC SYSTEMS

Volume 1

Corrigenda and Addenda

Page 76, foot of page:
the formula should read $X_L = 2\pi fL$

Page 100, line 5 should read:
with A in mm^2 and d in mm can be used.

Page 182, Fig.10.11
the filter section is a low-pass filter, so that a bar should be shown across the lower wave symbol.

Page 187, Fig.11.5
the arrows on the circles should point in the opposite directions.

Page 189, Fig.11.8
the direction of motion of the conductor should be to the left, at right angles to both flux and current.

P.191, Fig.11.11 last two lines of text should read
VOLTAGE + DIRECTION OF RESULTING
INTERNAL CURRENT (I) − INDEX

Page 207, Table 12.1 line 5
for 50 read to

Page 244: the tool-recognition test has now been replaced by a measurement exercise.

Servicing Electronic Systems

Volume 1

2nd Edition

A Textbook for the
City and Guilds of London Institute Course No. 224 (as revised 1989)

by

Ian R. Sinclair
B.Sc., M.I.E.E.

Formerly Lecturer in Physics & Electronics
Braintree (Essex) College of Further Education

and

Geoffrey E. Lewis
B.A., M.Sc., M.R.T.S., M.I.E.E.I.E.

Formerly Senior Lecturer in Radio, Television and Electronics,
Canterbury College of Technology

Avebury Technical

Second edition published 1991 by
Avebury Technical,
The Academic Publishing Group,
Gower House,
Croft Road,
Aldershot,
Hants GU11 3HR,
England

Gower Publishing Company,
Old Post Road,
Brookfield,
Vermont 05036,
USA.

British Library Cataloguing in Publication Data

Sinclair, Ian R. (Ian Richardson)
  Servicing electronic systems.–2nd. ed.
  Vol. 1
  1. Electronic equipment. Maintenance and repair
  I. Title   II. Lewis, Geoffrey E.   III. Sinclair, Ian R.
  (Ian Robertson) Electronics for the service
  engineer
  621.3810288

Library of Congress Cataloging-in-Publication Data

Sinclair, Ian R.
  Servicing electronic systems / by Ian R. Sinclair and Geoffrey E.
Lewis.–2nd ed.
    p.   cm.
  "A textbook for the City and Guilds of London Institute Course no.
224 (as revised 1989)."
    (pbk. : v. 1) : £9.95 (est.)
    1. Electronic systems–Maintenance and repair. I. Lewis
Geoffrey E. II. Title.
TK7870.S5242 1990
621.381–dc20   90–49889
                                                                 CIP

Printed and bound in Great Britain by
Billing & Sons Ltd, Worcester

Contents

Contents

Preface

As the end of the century approaches, the technology of electronics that was born in the twentieth century is now the dominant technology in all aspects of our lives. The very nature of electronics has changed enormously in our lifetimes, from its beginnings in radio to its involvement in control of everything from food mixers to car engine performance, from games to industrial empires.

All of this makes the task of servicing electronic equipment more specialized, more demanding and more important. Servicing personnel play a very important part in maintaining the correct operation of a system. They not only need to develop a high level of diagnostic skills but they also need to be able to communicate their findings to others so that the reliability and testability of a system can be improved. This then may also demand the further skills required to modify an in-service system. In particular, the training of anyone who will specialize in servicing must be geared to the speed and nature of the changes that are continually taking place. Such training must include a sound knowledge of principles and the development of diagnostic skills, neither of which is likely to be superseded by any changes in technology. Another important factor is that with the increasing harmonization of technical standards in Europe, it is likely that knowledge of technical terms in several European languages will become an essential part of the training for servicing work.

Although this series of books is designed primarily to cover the most recent requirements of the City and Guilds of London Institute Course No. 224 in Electronics Servicing, and also to provide coverage of the equivalent BTEC course, the books have been written mindful of the special needs of the home-based, distance learner. The approach is systems-based, viewing each electronic component or assembly as a device with known inputs and outputs. In this way, changes in technology do no require changes in the methods and principles of servicing, only to the everyday practical aspects which are continually changing in any case.

We have also taken every opportunity to look beyond the confines of the present syllabuses to the likely requirements of the future, and particularly to the impact of a single European market on both electronics and training. The books will invariably be amended in line with changes in the syllabuses and in the development of electronics, but the aim will be at all times to concentrate on the fundamentals of diagnosis and repair of whatever electronic equipment will require in years to come.

A guide book has been prepared which contains useful course hints and comments on the questions included in the main text. This booklet, which may be freely photocopied, is available free of charge to lecturers and instructors from:

Gower Publishing Co. Ltd,
Gower House,
Croft Road,
Aldershot,
Hampshire, GU11 3HR.

Other books in the *Servicing Electronic Systems* series that are in the course of preparation are:

Volume 2   Part 1 *Servicing Electronic Systems (Analogue & Digital Technology (Core Studies))*
Volume 2   Part 2 *Servicing Electronic Systems (Television & Radio Reception Technology)*
Volume 2   Part 3 *Servicing Electronic Systems (Control System Technology)*

Acknowledgements

The authors gratefully acknowledge the permission of the City and Guilds of London Institute to reproduce extracts from the Course No. 224, Electronics Servicing (New scheme) syllabus and regulations. An abridged version of the syllabus is included in the appendices and used as a cross reference to the contents of the various chapters. For precise details of the scheme, the reader is referred to the full Part 1 syllabus (CGJ 26320(M15)) available from the City and Guilds of London Institute, 76 Portland Place, London, W1N 4AA.

In addition, the authors would like formally to recognize the contributions of the following course tutors who made many useful and constructive criticisms of the previous series, *Electronics for the Service Engineer*: Steve Dennis, Brockenhurst College; M. Diplock, Eastbourne College of Advanced Technology; M. T. Dunn, Harlow College; N. R. Farrow, Norwich City College; A. Hynch, Weymouth College; Ian Oxenforth, North Lindsey College of Technology, Scunthorpe; D. A. Norman, East Herts College; Chris Parlett, Highlands College, Jersey; G. Rigby, Runshaw Tertiary College; John F. C. Smith, Cumbernauld College; John J. Stanton, W. R. Tuson College, Preston; B. Woodgate, South Downs College of Further Education, Havant.

1   The electronics industry

Refer to syllabus section 01

Objectives

The aims of this chapter are to allow the reader to obtain an understanding of the basic relations that exist between the electronics industry, national and international trading, the community in general and an individual employed within the industry.

By making vast quantities of information widely available the developments of the recent past in the electronics industry are having a massive impact on today's society. So much so, that the term *Information Technology* has been coined to describe this new dependant of the industry. The situation has arisen largely due to the convergence of microprocessor technology and telecommunications facilities. Such is this impact that it is important that students and technicians new to the industry have a working understanding of the way in which it interacts with today's society. There is one thing that the new entrant can be sure of, and that is that the industry will never be static. An indication of the wide range of employment opportunity and career development that exists, can be gained by dividing the industry into its five main areas of operations in the following manner:

(a)   Industrial and office electronics

(b) Military electronics
(c) Communications
(d) Domestic electronics
(e) Electronic components

of which only the first three remain predominantly British-owned. Industrial electronics is concerned with such topics as process control, which in turn is concerned with the monitoring of measurable quantities such as water purity, furnace temperatures, timing of critical operations, exhaust gas composition and so on. By using electronic methods which start with monitoring and end with controlling such quantities as volume of purifying gases, or the speed of feeding fuels, automation of processes can be achieved, and the study of robotics is now an important and rapidly expanding branch of electronics. Office electronics is much more recent, and has mainly been the result of the rapid development of microprocessors for small computers and fax machines as well as the use of older technology in tape recorders, answering machines and telephones.

Military electronics is concerned with both the defensive and the offensive aspects of electronics. The most important defensive application is early-warning radar, whether in fixed ground stations, in aircraft, or in satellites, and in infra-red detectors used in heat-seeking missiles that can be deployed against hostile aircraft. Offensive uses of electronics are concerned with the targeting of missiles, using stellar or satellite position fixing, the tracking of potential target aircraft, ships or tanks, and the detection of submarines.

Communications has in the past been the most important application of electronics, and the whole electronics industry arose from the invention of radio communications. The subject now covers the uses of electronics in non-entertainment radio and data transmission, satellite technology (including guidance), and the modern developments in telephone systems such as fibre-optic lines and repeater amplifiers.

Domestic electronics consists of TV and radio receivers, audio equipment and the very rapidly growing applications of home automation and car electronics. The high reliability of recent domestic electronics equipment has resulted in a reduction of the servicing hours needed, but this has been offset by the enormous growth in new applications such as CD players, satellite converters, music synthesizers, crime detection electronics, portable telephones, small computers, 'smart' machines (washing machines, toasters, irons) and car engine control systems.

The electronics components industry has declined seriously, and to some extent because of ill thought-out legislation to protect it rather than to modernize it. Virtually all electronics components now have to be imported into the UK, and tariffs that were designed to protect the industry now have the effect of making it more expensive to assemble electronics equipment in the UK than to

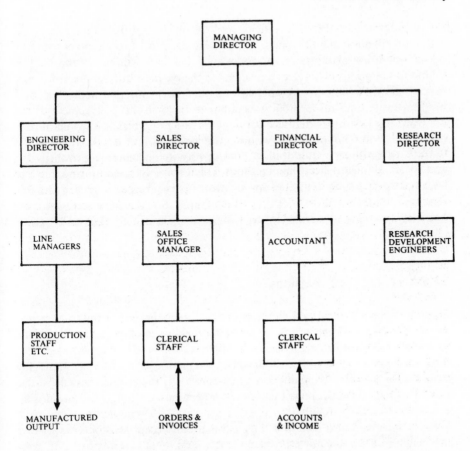

Figure 1.1 Notional structure of a manufacturing company

assemble abroad and import completed items. Though some components can be obtained in Europe, many items such as specialized integrated circuits (ICs) have to be imported if the electronics industry is to continue making anything in the UK.

Organization of the electronics industry

Figure 1.1 shows the theoretical structure of a manufacturing organization that is typical of the electronics industry. The managing director has overall day-to-day control over the running of the business and he, in turn, would normally be responsible to the board of directors and ultimately, the shareholders. Because of the wide-ranging skills required to run such a company, each branch is

3

managed by a specialist in the field, and he or she controls that particular section through the separate managers who have a more direct contact with the specific operation of that section. These staff members will be responsible for production of goods or services particular to the business and for ensuring that the invoices and bills are despatched and that payments are made. Lines of communication and responsibility usually run through this hierarchical structure from top to bottom and vice versa. A retailing organization would have a similar structure but probably without the research and development limb. Apart from the direct responsibility of both employer and employee towards the efficient running of the business, each must be aware of any dangerous situations that can arise and take appropriate protective actions. It is written into the Health and Safety at Work Act that all personnel should ensure and guard the health and safety of all within the organization and visitors to the site, by using safe working practices.

Customer and staff relations

An important, but at times difficult, point to remember, is that the customer is the reason for the organization being in business in the first place. Therefore good customer relations are essential if a firm is to remain in business. The new customer's first contact will most likely be through the sales or service staff who should have a courteous manner. The customer's first impressions will be the longest lasting and thus create the basis or otherwise for a long association. The firm must provide a reliable product or service, with reliable and consistent delivery dates and at a cost that the customer can accept as economical. At a later stage in the association problems might arise that can involve staff from other departments. These individuals should show a sympathetic response to the problem and liaise with the client in a courteous manner. When developing new products or services it is often good practice to involve the most likely customers at an early stage of development. They then feel that their contribution and custom is appreciated. In return, the good customer shows appreciation by the prompt payment of bills and by providing further orders for goods or services. A satisfied customer is the best and cheapest form of advertising that an organization can have.

Within the working environment, good inter-staff relations are particularly important to the success of a business. These can be achieved by ensuring that each employee obtains job satisfaction, is provided with a good working environment and is given good training. Within the organization, there should exist a chain of good communications to ensure that consultations can resolve difficult personnel and production problems. The employees' remunerations can usefully include incentive schemes, pension and health care schemes, and in suitable businesses, allow them to become share-owning members of the organization. Taken together, points such as these will go a long way to ensuring a mutual loyalty between employer and employee, that can only benefit the business.

Effects of international trade in electronic goods

With international trading, the provision of goods and services at an economical rate or price is even more important than in the home market. To be able to sell a product overseas at high cost, the product or the supporting technology must be unique and not available elsewhere. Thus home producers of export electronic equipment not only have to be very competitive on cost, but must also have carefully researched the foreign market-place to ensure that the product will sell. Overseas producers will try to sell goods into the home market for a number of reasons. When production can be carried out in a country with low labour costs, goods can be cheaper than when home-produced. Alternatively goods can be sold at a loss just to obtain currency that can be traded elsewhere in the world at a profit. On a more sinister note, it has not been unknown for the home production of a particular line of goods to be destroyed by cheap imports, initially sold at a loss. When the home production collapses, the overseas supplier then increases his prices to recoup his losses, without competition from the home producer. The international organization GATT (General Agreement on Tariffs and Trade) was devised to control such *dumping* to minimize these unwanted effects on world trade. Tariffs are an import tax imposed on goods from abroad, so as to artificially load the costs in favour of local production. Such protection for the home producer can however have a negative effect. The isolation of providing goods or services to a home market only, prevents business from developing along with that of the foreign competitors.

Contributions by the electronics industry to the national economy

The wide-ranging applications of electronic goods and components means that other sections of industry are becoming dependent on new technology. This greater usage of electronics leads to a larger highly skilled work force that has many implications for the national economy. Financially, industry contributes to the exchequer income by paying value added tax (VAT) on its purchases, income tax on its profits, plus a range of sales taxes on specific items such as motor cars. For the exchequer, the larger work force means greater income from individual income tax and VAT, plus the reduced costs for unemployment and various social applications. Since this leads to more money in the economy, consumers then purchase a wider range of luxury goods, very often

5

electronic-based, which leads to a further expansion in the electronics industry. An export market not only increases production, sales and hence income; it also provides work for the transportation and insurance industries, all helping to further increase the size of the work force and in turn increase the wealth of the nation.

Electronics and the community

Contribution to the local environment

The electronics industry provides employment for personnel with a very wide range of skills and abilities, both male and female. For the newcomer, the job opportunities and promotional prospects are most rewarding, because the industry is continually developing new technologies and concepts, which involves almost continuous training and retraining. This challenging work is almost always carried out in a comfortable environment.

Outside the industry, many people are provided with entertainment, safety, labour-saving and security equipment. A ready means of communication is provided so that even the domestic television receiver can become a centre for the distribution of information as well as entertainment. The TV set can be interconnected with the telephone or a computer to provide either leisure services or to connect the home to the office or works computer system. This concept can be extended very easily to allow work such as data preparation and desk-top publishing to be carried out at home. This reduces the amount of time wasted in travelling, avoids the stress of traffic rush hours, and should help to make for a more sedate lifestyle. Teleshopping and telebanking are just two of the services that are available to the customer to extend the labour-saving facilities. In certain industrial processes electronically controlled robots can carry out tasks in environments that would be unacceptable to human beings.

Broadcasting services

Public service broadcasting is a resource that can be used not only for entertainment, but also for information and education, particularly in such cases as illiteracy and drug abuse. Such programmes can only be financially supported by funds through a central authority and provided indirectly by receiver licensing. In the UK most commercial television is supported by advertising fees charged for the inserts during natural breaks in programmes. Sponsorship of special programmes, such as sporting events, has its origins in North America but is gradually appearing in Europe. Again, the sponsor's returns are due to the advertising feature of the concept.

With the developments that are occurring in digital processing, the possibility of signal scrambling and encryption provides a further source of funding for television programmes. The viewer has to obtain the descrambling key from the programme provider, but at a fee. This may be payable on a subscription basis to the whole output of a particular channel, or on a payment for a specific programme. This concept is described as *pay-per-view*. The expansion of such services through satellite links provides much additional work and income for the electronics industry.

In most countries, the quality and content of television programmes is monitored and controlled by a government-appointed body.

Questions suitable for group discussion

Do computers need people more than people need computers?
Is 'homeworking' a desirable situation?
Does subsidization of a home product prove advantageous in the long run?
In a rapidly changing industry, who should pay for retraining?
Is public service broadcasting necessary, or should all programmes be provided by advertising or subscription?
What are the implications of the Data Protection Act?
Can information be too freely available?
What are the main problems involved with electronic fund transfer?

2 Safety at work

Refer to syllabus section 02

Chapter summary

Safety policy – duties of employers and employees. Safety legislation in the UK and the rest of Europe. Electrical safety. Fire precautions and emergency procedures. Toxic substances in electronics work. Safe working methods. First aid and incident reporting.

Electronic servicing, like any other practical activity, must be carried out in a way that ensures maximum safety for the employee and for anyone else present. In the UK, the Health and Safety at Work Act of 1974, which came into full operation in October 1978, laid down that employees (including students) also have a duty to observe all the safety precautions that have been laid down by their employers, and to carry out all work in a safe way. The Act greatly expands provisions that were made in the various Factory Acts up to and including 1961, and further provisions for the reporting of accidents at work have been made in the Notification of Accidents and General Occurrences Regulations of 1980.

The Act is a long document written in legal language, but its intentions can be summarized as:

1 All employers, including teachers, tutors and instructors, must ensure that

8

any apparatus to be used or serviced by employees or students is as safe to operate as it can be made. Equipment which cannot be made safe should be used only under close supervision.

2 Employers, tutors and instructors must make sure that employees and students at all times make use of the required safety equipment such as protective clothing, goggles, ear protectors etc. which must be provided for them.

3 Employees and students must ensure that they carry out all their work in such a way that it does not endanger them, people working around them, or the subsequent users of equipment that they repair.

4 Any accidents must be logged and reported, and measures taken to ensure that such incidents cannot happen again.

To comply with these general requirements of the Act, employers, instructors, employees and students must possess a good working knowledge of the dangers that exist, as well as of safety procedures which need to be observed to keep these risks to a minimum. The rest of this chapter will be devoted to the problems of general workshop safety, hazards that are particularly important for electronics servicing work, and to an explanation of safe working methods generally. One of the difficulties in enforcing safe working methods on anyone involved in electronics servicing is the wide variety of working places, which can vary from a well-designed workshop, as safe as possible in the light of current experience, to a home in which a TV receiver has failed, and in which almost every possible hazard, from bad electrical wiring to the presence of children around the TV receiver, exists. This huge difference in working conditions makes it vital for anyone working on electronics servicing to be aware of safe working methods and to practise them at all times whether supervised or not.

The emphasis of all health and safety legislation is on accident prevention as well as on dealing with accidents. Dealing with accidents is a matter of provision of facilities for, mainly, first aid and fire fighting and is very much in the hands of the employer. Prevention of accidents depends on attitudes of mind and is the responsibility of everyone concerned. Accident prevention depends on:

- the recognition of hazards
- the elimination of hazards
- the replacement of hazards
- guarding and/or marking hazards
- a sense of personal protection
- continuing education in safety.

All these call for the full cooperation of all concerned. Ten people might walk past a large packing-case, and only one recognize the difficulty that it would present in an evacuation for a fire, or see the nails sticking out of the case that could maim an arm. Hazard recognition is the most difficult part of safety, because we tend to take hazards for granted, or to ignore them. Once a hazard has been recognized, its presence must be logged, and then thought can be given to eliminating it (move the packing-case, hammer the nails down) or one of the other possibilities. A dangerous power tool can often be replaced with one that uses a safer principle, for example, the old-style guillotine cutter has been replaced by the roller-type for offices. An unavoidable projection from a wall can be painted to make it more visible, or a guard put around it. Lines can be drawn on a factory floor to show safe walking areas.

All these are comparatively simple methods of dealing with hazards, providing that the hazard has been recognized in the first place. The person who recognizes a hazard is the person who can imagine what might happen if an emergency arose, or who knows how to look for danger. These attitudes can be cultivated, because we would not have survived thus far as a species if we did not have some consciousness of danger.

Responsibilities

Safety legislation calls for both employer and employee to observe safe working practices and to strive at all times to improve safety standards. Self-employed persons are responsible for their own safety and the safety of anyone who works alongside them, and they also have a responsibility to avoid endangering members of the public. The self-employed should ensure that they have insurance protection against claims (third-party claims) from the public, and for work outside the UK they must ensure also that their qualifications entitle them to be carrying out the grade of work which they are undertaking.

The employer

The responsibilities of an employer are:

1 To provide a safe place of work with no hazards from insecure floors, leaking roofs, blocked windows, restricted doorways and so on.
2 To provide safe plant and equipment, so that work benches and equipment are adequate for the job, and all tools are fitted with safety guards. Larger power tools should be screened or fenced, and where relevant floors should have safe walking areas marked out.
3 To provide safe working systems, so that employees do not have to use makeshift equipment or methods. Protective clothing should be provided if needed.
4 To provide safe surroundings at a reasonable working temperature with control of humidity if needed, and good ventilation. Employees should not

be subjected to dust and fumes, and there must be washing facilities, sanitation for both men and women, and provision for first aid in the event of an accident.

5   To ensure safety in the handling, storing and movement of goods. Employees should not be required to lift heavy loads (in some EEC countries, the amount that an employee can be expected to lift without assistance is limited to 15 kg), and mechanical handling must be provided where heavy loads are commonplace. Dangerous materials must be identified and stored where they do not cause any hazard to anyone on the site.

6   To provide a system for logging and reporting accidents.

7   To provide information, training and updating of training in safety precautions, along with supervision that will ensure safety.

8   To devise and administer a safety policy that can be reviewed by representatives of both employer and employees.

These rules are reasonably straightforward to interpret where servicing is carried out in a central workshop, but one of the problems of electronic servicing arises because work often has to be carried out at the premises of a customer rather than in specialized workshops. Where the servicing is done on industrial premises, the general conditions should be to much the same standard as in any other workshop, but electronics equipment will not necessarily be located in conditions that are suitable for servicing. In such circumstances, employers should:

(a)   ensure that servicing is carried out by staff who are adequately qualified and experienced (this is a legal necessity in Germany and Holland);

(b)   ensure that more than one person is present if this would contribute to added safety;

(c)   make full use of replaceable sub-assemblies so that detailed work can be carried out in the workshop rather than at the site.

The current trend to replace printed boards rather than to locate individual faults makes servicing on site rather easier and safer than it once was, but the problem remains that neither employer nor employee has full control over working conditions on a remote site. The employer should ensure that the site owner will provide for safe working as far as is practicable, and the employees must also try to ensure that they use safe working methods.

The worst possible working conditions are in the home. Wiring may be unsound, with poor earthing, overloaded cables, no fire precautions, badly arranged working space and even the presence of children. Unless the servicing job is particularly simple and can be carried out quickly, it is always desirable to remove the equipment to work on to the workshop. Many TV and audio servicing specialists make this a general rule, even if equipment (which must be

11

in safe working condition) has to be left on loan to replace the equipment which is being serviced. No attempt should ever be made to carry out major work on TV and audio equipment in a customer's home unless there is absolutely no alternative. Some domestic equipment (mainly TV receivers and high-quality loudspeakers) are both bulky and heavy, and help will be needed to move them into a van.

The employee

The employer is made responsible in law for ensuring that safe working is possible and ensuring that each employee is aware of safe methods. The law recognizes, however, the difficulty of forcing an employee to work in a safe way, so that the employee also has responsibilities to ensure safe working. This applies to fellow workers and to members of the public as well as to personal safety. This part of safety legislation is harder to define because most accidents are caused by human carelessness in one form or another and though it is possible to draw up standards for safe methods of working, it is impossible to ensure that everyone will abide by these standards at all times.

The employees' responsibilities, which apply also to the self-employed, include:

- Taking care of their own health so that safety is not jeopardized. This means avoiding the use of alcohol or drugs if their effects would still be present in working hours. In some countries, blood alcohol level can be checked following industrial accidents as well as following a road accident. Working while excessively tired can also be a cause of accidents due to relaxed vigilance. Remember that the term 'drugs' can include such items as painkillers, anti-histamines for hay-fever, and anti-depressants.
- Ensuring that clothing is such as to provide reasonable protection, with no loose materials that can be caught in machinery or even (as has been reported) melted and set alight by a soldering iron. Long hair is even more dangerous in this respect, and must be fastened so that it cannot be caught.
- Behaving in a way that contributes to safety. Carelessness and recklessness cannot be tolerated, and practical jokes do not belong in any workplace. Once again, legislation in several countries treats this type of behaviour in the workplace as seriously as it is treated on the roads.
- Ensuring that the work they are doing is within their competence. This means that the employee must know, either from experience, discussion with a colleague, or from reference to manuals, what has to be done and the safe way of carrying out the work. In several EEC countries, it is an offence to carry out work for which you are not qualified, and if you are working abroad you will have to find out to what extent UK qualifica-

tions apply in other countries.

- Ensuring that nothing they can do can be a hazard to others. This spans a very wide range of behaviour from the way that a van is driven to carelessness with a soldering iron. Self-employed service personnel should insure against third-party claims, and employees must remember that they can be sued if their careless or reckless behaviour leads to injury. Misusing safety equipment is a criminal offence, quite apart from endangering the lives of others.

General safety

Apart from electrical safety problems, most of the main everyday workshop hazards arise from the handling of tools of all kinds but especially of machine tools. There is a right way, and several wrong ways, of using anything from a screwdriver to a power drill, and safe methods of working must always be used especially when you are in a hurry. Sharp tools like screwdrivers should never be used in such a way that they can pierce the skin if they slip from the work. One common example is using a screwdriver to unscrew a wire from a plug that is held in the palm of the hand rather than between fingers or, better still, in a vice.

Small tools have to be suited to the job and used correctly. Never use a blade screwdriver when a Philips or Pozidrive type is needed, and remember that screwdriver size must be matched to the work. Files should be fitted with handles and used with care because, being brittle, they can snap. Never use a file as a tommy-bar, for instance. Box spanners and socket sets should be used in preference to open spanners where possible.

Power tools must be electrically safe. They should always be disconnected when adjustments have to be made such as changing speed or changing drill bits, and they should never be used unless the correct guards and other protective devices have been carefully fitted to them and around them. The mains leads to power tools must be in perfect condition, with no fraying or kinking, and should be renewed if necessary. Metal tools should be earthed, and in some conditions can be powered from isolating transformers – another option is to use only battery-powered tools. Most domestic power tools use plastic casings with double insulation, but these are not necessarily suitable for industrial uses.

Protective clothing should be worn wherever the regulations or plain common sense demands it. The workshop is no place for loose ties or cravats, for long untied hair or strings of beads. A workshop coat or boiler suit should be worn whenever workshop tools are being used, and eyeshields or goggles are nearly always necessary. Goggles and gloves must always be worn when cathode-ray tubes are being handled and safety boots should be worn when heavy objects have to be moved.

Even operations as common as snipping wire with side-cutters can be a hazard to the eyes, either of the user of the cutters or of anyone standing close, and goggles should be worn by anyone who is working close to such operations, particularly if hard wire like Nichrome is being snipped. Ideally, the wire which is being snipped should be secured at both ends so that no loose bits can fly around – one safe method is to hold the main part of the wire in a vice and the other part in a Mole-wrench.

Test equipment must be electrically safe, using earthing or double insulation as appropriate. Here also, the use of battery-operated equipment can lead to much safer use. Where mains-operated test equipment is used, the mains voltage setting must be suitable, the power leads in good condition, and the fusing correct for the load (usually 3A). All test equipment, particularly if used on servicing live equipment, should be subject to safety checks at regular intervals, and users should maintain such equipment carefully, avoiding mechanical or electrical damage.

Soldering and de-soldering present hazards which are peculiar to the electronics workshop. The soldering iron should always be kept in a covered holder to prevent accidental contact with hands or cables. Many electrical fires are started by a soldering iron falling on to its own cable or the cable of another power tool or instrument. Though it can be very convenient to hang an iron up on a piece of metal, the use of a proper stand with a substantial heat sink is the safe method that ought to be used.

In use, excessive solder should be wiped from the iron with a damp cloth rather than by being flicked off and scattered around the workshop. During de-soldering, drops of solder should not be allowed to drip from a joint; they should be gathered up on the iron and then wiped off it, or sucked up by a de-soldering gun which is equipped with a solder pump.

Care should be taken to avoid breathing in the fumes from hot flux. Where soldering is carried out on a routine basis, an extractor hood should be used to ensure that fumes are efficiently removed. Materials other than soldering flux can cause fumes, and some types of plastics, particularly the PTFE types of materials and the vinyls, can give off very toxic fumes if they are heated to high temperatures. Extraction can help here, but it is preferable to use careful methods of working which ensure that these materials are not heated.

The single most common cause of absence from work in the UK is back injury, mostly caused by incorrect methods of lifting heavy objects or holding such objects before putting them into place. In the course of electronics servicing work many large and heavy items have to be shifted. The correct method of lifting is to keep a straight back throughout the whole of the lifting operation, bending your knees as necessary but never your back. Never attempt to shift anything heavy by yourself. Even if you bear all the weight of carrying a load, help in lifting and steering the load can make the difference between safe and unsafe work. In several countries, there is a statutory upper limit of load that one operator is allowed to lift, and this can be as low as 15 kg (33 lbs).

Workshop benches and stools should be constructed so that excessive lifting is not required, and if a large number of heavy items have to be moved to and from benches, mechanical handling equipment should be used. Stool heights should be adjustable so that no user need stoop for long periods to work on equipment.

Reporting of both accidents and hazards is most important. Though it is primarily the responsibility of an employer to ensure that a workspace is kept free of dangerous and badly sited materials, those who work in that space are the first to know when a hazard exists, and should make the first notification – you cannot take the attitude that it will be the fault of someone else if an accident happens. Two logbooks should be maintained, one for reporting potential hazards so that action can be taken (or if the worst happens, blame apportioned), and the other to record actual accidents, so that a written account is available of every incident. By frequent reference to these logs, safety policies can be amended as required to ensure that better ways of dealing with hazards are developed.

To sum up, the general rules for the employee are:

- to be alert to hazards
- to maintain personal hygiene, fitness, and tidiness
- to protect yourself and others from injury
- to know the emergency procedures thoroughly
- to report all hazards and accidents as soon as possible.

Electrical safety

The main electrical hazard in servicing operations is working on live equipment, because this presents the risk of shock. Electric shock is caused by current flowing through the body, and it is the amount of current and where it flows that is important. The resistance of the body is not constant so that the amount of current that can flow for a given voltage will vary according to the moistness of the skin. The most important hazard is of electric current flowing through the heart. Ways of avoiding this include the following:

1   Ensure that only low voltages (less than 50V) are present in a circuit.
2   Ensure that no currents exceeding 1 mA can flow in any circumstances.
3   Keep your hands dry at all times, because moist hands conduct much better than dry hands.
4   Keep workshop floors dry, and wear rubber-soled shoes or boots.
5   Avoid two-handed actions, particularly if one hand can touch a circuit and the other hand is touching a metal chassis, metal bench or any other metal object.

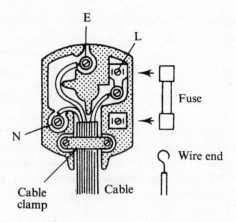

Figure 2.1   A standard three-pin plug (with cover removed)

Table 2.1   Colour codes for flexible wiring

	Live	Neutral	Earth
Current colours	Brown	Blue	Green and yellow
Old colours	Red	Black	Green

For most people the heart is on the left side of the chest and this makes it safer to work with the right hand only, making a longer electrical path to the heart in the event of touching live connections. At low voltages, the resistance of the human body is normally high enough to ensure that only small currents can flow through the skin. If the equipment contains points at which higher voltages are present but where the source resistance is high so that any current that can flow will be small then this also can be acceptable.

The greatest hazard in most electronic servicing is the mains supply which in the UK and in most of Europe is at 240V a.c. Three connections are made at the usual UK domestic supply socket, labelled live (L), neutral (N) and earth (E) respectively. The live contact at 240V can pass current to either of the other two. The neutral connection provides the normal return path for current with the earth connection used as an emergency path for returning current in the event of a fault. Earth leakage contact breakers (ELCBs) work by detecting any small current through the earth line and using this to operate a relay that will open the live connection, cutting off the supply. Connection to domestic supplies is made by a three-pin plug, shown opened in Figure 2.1. This plug is designed so that shutters within the socket are raised only when the plug is correctly inserted.

Details of the wire connections within the plug are shown, and Table 2.1 lists the colour codings of the wire connections to the plug. Though it is many years

Table 2.2   Standard fuse sizes and colours

Value	Colour	Applications
3A	Red	All domestic electronic equipment; test gear.
13A	Brown	Heaters and kettles

since the coding colours were changed, older equipment can still be found bearing the older colours. Particular care should be taken in working on cables which have been colour-coded to foreign standards, though by the mid-1990s all European equipment should be using the same codings. The older colours are still used in internal domestic wiring to sockets.

A plug must be wired so that:

(a)   The cable is firmly held and clamped without damaging the insulation or the conductors.

(b)   All connections are tight with no loose strands of wire. The ends of the cable can be coated with solder to prevent loose strands from separating, but the soldered end should not be used for clamping because the wire is more brittle and will loosen off after some time.

(c)   The wires should be cut so that the live lead will break and pull free before the earth lead if there is excessive force on the cable.

(d)   A fuse of the correct rating must be used. The standard fuse ratings for domestic equipment are 3A, colour-coded red, and 13A, colour-coded brown. Most domestic electronic equipment can use the 3A rated fuses, and the few items that require a larger fuse should preferably be used with a (non-standard) 7A fuse rather than the 13A type, because the appliance cables for such equipment are seldom rated for 13A (see Table 2.2).

(e)   The cable should be clamped where it enters the equipment, or alternatively a plug and socket of the standard type can be used so that the mains lead consists of a domestic plug at one end and a eurosocket (never a plug) at the other.

Note: Non-domestic equipment often makes use of standard domestic plugs, but where higher-power electronic equipment is in use the plugs and socket will generally be of types designed for higher voltages and current, often for 3-phase 440V a.c. In some countries, flat two-pin plugs and sockets are in use, with no earth provision except for cookers and washing machines, though by the end of the century uniform standards should prevail in Europe, certainly for new buildings.

The circuit should also include:

(a)   A fuse whose rating matches the consumption of the equipment. This fuse may have blowing characteristics that differ from those of the fuse in the plug. It may, for example, be a fast-blowing type which will blow when submitted to a brief overload, or it may be of the slow-blow type that will withstand a mild overload for a period of several minutes.

(b) A double-pole switch that breaks both live and neutral lines. The earth line must never be broken by a switch.

(c) A mains-warning light or indicator which is connected between the live and neutral lines.

All these items should be checked as part of any servicing operation, on a routine basis. As far as possible all testing should be done on equipment that is disconnected and switched off. The absence of a pilot light or the fact that a switch is in the OFF position should never be relied on. Mains-powered equipment in particular should be completely isolated by unplugging from the mains. If the equipment is, like most non-domestic equipment, permanently wired then the fuses in the supply line must be removed before the covers are taken from the equipment. Many pieces of industrial electronics equipment have safety switches built into the covers so that the mains supply is switched off at more than one point when the covers are removed.

The ideal to be aimed at is that only low-voltage battery-operated equipment should be operated on when live. When mains-powered equipment must unavoidably be tested live, the meter, oscilloscope or other instrument(s) should not be connected until the equipment is switched off and isolated, and the live terminals should be covered before the supply voltage is restored. The supply line should be isolated again before the meter or other instrument clips are removed.

The main dangers of working on live circuits are:

1 The risk of fatal shock through touching high-voltage exposed terminals which can pass large currents through the body.

2 The risk of fatal shock from the discharge of capacitors that were previously charged to a high voltage.

3 The risk of damage to instruments or to the operator when a mild electric shock is experienced. The uncontrollable muscular jerking which is caused by an electric shock of any kind can cause the operator to drop meters, to lose his/her balance and fall on to other, possibly more dangerous equipment.

4 Even low-voltage circuits can be dangerous because of the high temperatures which can be momentarily generated when a short circuit occurs. These temperatures can cause burning, sometimes severe. As a precaution, chains, watch-straps and rings made of metal should not be worn while servicing is being carried out.

There is one type of danger which is peculiar to the older type of TV receivers

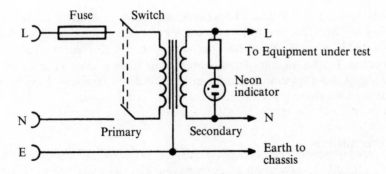

Figure 2.2   How an isolating transformer should be connected

and to some very old AC/DC mains radios. These devices used 'live chassis' circuits in which the neutral lead of the mains supply was connected to the metal chassis of the equipment. Incorrect wiring of the plug or a disconnected neutral lead can then cause the chassis to become live at full supply voltage. Even some later models of TV receiver which use considerably lower internal voltages still use a live-chassis approach, and some have the chassis at about half of supply voltage.

Live working on such equipment should never be carried out without the use of an isolating transformer with the chassis securely earthed. A safe type of connection is illustrated in Figure 2.2.

Soldering should never be carried out on any equipment, whether the chassis is live or not, until the chassis has been completely disconnected from the mains supply and all capacitors safely discharged. The metal tip of the soldering iron will normally be earthed, and should not be allowed to come into contact with any metalwork that is connected to the neutral line of the mains, because large currents can flow between neutral and earth. Obviously, any contact between the soldering iron and the live supply should also be avoided.

Other electrical safety points

(a) Cables must never be allowed to fray or split, nor be sharply bent, too tightly clamped or cut. Damaged cables must be renewed at once. Hot soldering irons must be kept well away from cable insulation.

(b) Cables must be securely fastened both into plugs and into powered equipment. The supply cable to a heavy piece of equipment should be connected by way of a plug and socket which will part if the cable is pulled. The live end of the connector must have no pins which can be touched.

(c) Every electrical joint should be mechanically as well as electrically sound. It must be well secured with no danger of working loose and with no stray pieces of wire.

(d) The old-fashioned type of lead-acid accumulator releases an explosive mixture of hydrogen and oxygen while it is on charge, and this can be ignited by a spark. No attempt should ever be made to connect or disconnect such accumulators from a charger or from a load while current is flowing. An explosion is serious enough, but the explosive spray of acid along with sharp glass or plastic fragments is even worse.

Fire precautions

Workshop fires present several types of hazard. The obvious one is flesh burns, but injuries from other causes are even more common, such as falling when running from a burning workshop. Clear escape routes should be marked and these must be kept clear at all times.

A fire can start wherever there is material that can burn (combustible material), air that can supply oxygen for burning, and any hot object that can raise the temperature of materials to the burning point. A fire can be extinguished by removing all combustible material, by removing the supply of air (oxygen) or by cooling the material to below the burning temperature. The most dangerous fires are those in which the burning material can supply its own oxygen (such materials are classed as explosives) and in which the burning material is a liquid that can flow about the workplace taking the fire with it.

Another major danger is of asphyxiation from the fumes produced by the fire. In electronics workshops the materials that are used as switch cleaners, the wax in capacitors, the plastics casings, the insulation of transformers and the selenium that can still be found in some old-fashioned metal rectifiers will all produce dangerous fumes, either choking or toxic, when burning. Good ventilation can reduce much of this particular hazard.

The key points for fire safety are:

(a) Good maintenance
(b) No naked flames and no smoking permitted
(c) Tidy working, with no accumulation of rubbish
(d) Clearly marked escape paths in case of fire
(e) Good ventilation to reduce the build-up of dangerous fumes
(f) Suitable fire extinguishers in clearly marked positions
(g) Knowledge by all staff of how to deal with fire/explosion
(h) Regular fire drills and inspection of equipment.

Because of the variety of materials that can cause a fire, more than one method of extinguishing a fire may have to be used, and use of the wrong type of extinguisher can sometimes make a fire worse. The five main types of fire extinguisher and their colour-coding are (a) water-based (red), (b) foam (cream)

(c) powder (blue), (d) CO_2 (carbon dioxide) gas (black), (e) inert liquid (green).

The water-based type of extinguisher (for a Class A fire) is most effective on materials that absorb water and which will be cooled easily. Fires in paper, wood or cloth are best tackled in this way, using the extinguisher on the base of the fire to wet materials that are not yet burning and to cool materials that have caught light. Water-based extinguishers must never be used on electrical fires or on fires that occur near to electrical equipment.

Class B fires involve burning liquids or materials that will melt to liquids when hot. The main hazards here are fierce flames as the heat vaporizes the liquid, and the ease with which the fire can spread so as to affect other materials. The most effective treatment is to remove the air supply by smothering the fire, and the foam, dry powder or CO_2 gas extinguishers can all be useful, though gas extinguishers should be used so that the foam, powder or gas falls down on to the fire, because if you direct the extinguisher at the base of this type of fire the liquid will often simply float away, still burning. Fire blankets can be effective on small fires of this type, but on larger fires there is a risk that the blanket will act as a wick, encouraging the fire by allowing the burning liquid to spread.

For dealing with electrical fires, the water-or foam-based types should be avoided because the risk of electric shock caused by the conduction of the water or foam is often more serious than the effect of a small fire. Inert liquid extinguishers are effective on electrical fires but the liquids can generate toxic fumes and can also dissolve some insulating materials. Powder extinguishers and CO_2 types are very effective on small fires of the type that are likely to develop in electronics workshops. They must be inspected and check-weighed regularly to ensure that internal pressure is being maintained.

A few sand-buckets are also desirable. They must be kept full of clean sand and never used as ashtrays or for waste materials. A fire-mat is also an important accessory in the event of setting fire to the clothing of anyone in the workshop. The fire-mat should be kept in a prominent place and everyone in the workshop should know how to use it.

In the event of a fire, your order of priorities should be:

1 To raise the alarm and call the fire brigade even if you think you can tackle the fire.
2 To try to ensure evacuation of the workshop.
3 To make use of the appropriate fire extinguishers.

The important point here is that you must never try to fight a fire alone, nor to put others at risk by failing to sound the alarm. The most frightening aspect of fire is the way that a small flame can in a few seconds become a massive conflagration, completely out of hand, and though prompt use of an extinguisher might stop the fire at an early stage, raising the alarm and calling for assistance is more important.

Toxic materials

Virtually every workplace contains toxic materials, or materials that can become toxic in some circumstances, such as a fire. Industrial solvents, such as are used for cleaning electronics sub-assemblies, switch contacts etc. are often capable of causing asphyxiation and even in small concentrations can cause drowsiness and stupor. Many common insulating materials are safe at normal temperatures, but can give off toxic fumes when hot.

In addition, some very poisonous materials are used within electronics components. Such materials can be found in cathode-ray tubes, fluorescent tubes, valves, metal rectifiers, electrolytic capacitors and other items. The local hospital should be informed of the toxic materials that are present, and if possible should advise on any first aid that might be effective in the event of these materials being released. In particular, cathode-ray tubes and fluorescent tubes must be handled with care because they present the hazard of flying glass as well as of toxic materials if they are shattered.

Transistors and ICs should never in any circumstances be cut open. No servicing operation would ever call for this to be done, but if a faulty component has to be cut away there might be a danger of puncturing it. Some power transistors, particularly those used on transmitters, contain the solid material beryllium oxide whose dust is extremely poisonous if inhaled, even in very small quantities. All such transistors that have to be replaced should be removed very carefully from their boards and returned to the manufacturers for safe disposal.

Corrosive chemicals form another class of toxic material which cause severe damage to the skin on contact. Sulphuric acid has the effect of removing water from the skin, causing severe burning, whereas sodium hydroxide (caustic soda) dissolves fatty materials and thus damages the skin by removal of fat. All strongly acidic or alkaline materials will cause severe skin damage on contact, but by far the most dangerous in addition to sulphuric acid and sodium hydroxide are hydrofluoric acid (used for etching glass) and nitric acid (used in etching copper). The only first aid treatment is to apply large amounts of water to dilute the corrosive material. Even very dilute acids or alkalis will cause severe damage if they reach the eye, and once again, large amounts of pure water should be applied as a first aid measure. Never attempt to neutralize one chemical with another, because neutralization is usually accompanied by the generation of heat. Specialized treatment at hospital should always be sought in any case of accident with corrosive materials.

First aid

In every workshop at least one person, and preferably two, should be trained in first aid procedures. This does not necessarily mean elaborate treatment, because the day-to-day hazards of minor cuts and burns can be covered simply enough with the aid of a fairly basic first aid chest along with good facilities for washing, but accidents that involve toxic materials or fumes call for much more specialized equipment and knowledge. It is particularly important never to work alone with potentially toxic materials. First aid training should, of course, cover the handling of electric shock. The important point is that before anything else can be done, the supply must be cut off. The victim must never be approached before this is done, otherwise there may be two victims instead of one. Mouth-to-mouth resuscitation, preferably by way of a plastic disposable mouthpiece, should then be applied as soon as the power is off, and continued until the victim is breathing or until an ambulance arrives. If too much time would be wasted in locating and operating a mains switch, the victim should be pushed away from live wires using any insulated materials, such as a dry broomhandle, or pulled away by gripping clothing. The important point is not to touch the skin of the victim – not only is there a danger to the rescuer but more danger to the victim because of the additional current that will flow, perhaps through the heart.

Speedy action is important, because the brain can be irreparably damaged after about four minutes even if breathing can be restored. Always leave an unconscious victim on his/her side, never on the back or on the face. Never try to administer brandy or any other liquid to anyone who is not fully conscious because the risk of choking to death is at least as great as that of electric shock itself.

Once the victim has been removed from the danger of continued shock, mouth-to-mouth resuscitation can be given. Practical experience in this work is essential; it cannot be learned from a book, but a summary will remind you of the steps:

1 Place the victim on his/her back, loosen clothing around the neck, remove any items such as false teeth or chewing gum from the mouth.
2 Tip the head back by putting one of your hands under the neck and the other on the forehead. This opens the breathing passages.
3 Pinch the nose to avoid air leakage, breathe in deeply, and blow the air out into the victim's lungs. If possible, use an approved mouth-to-mouth adapter to avoid any risk of transferring disease, but never waste time looking for one.
4 Release your mouth and watch the victim breathe out – you may have to assist by pressing on the chest.
5 Repeat at a slow breathing rate until help arrives or the victim can breathe unattended. Do not give up just because the victim is not breathing after a few minutes because your efforts can sustain life and avoid brain damage even if the victim is unconscious for hours.

Electric shock is often accompanied by the symptoms of burning which will also have to be treated, though not so urgently. The workshop telephone should have permanently placed next to it a list of the numbers of emergency services such as doctors on call, ambulance, fire, chemists, hospital casualty units, police, and any specialized services such as burns and shock units. The list should be typed or printed legibly, maintained up to date and stuck securely to a piece of plywood or hardboard. The checking of this list for position, legibility and updating should form part of any safety inspection.

Severe burning must be treated quickly at a hospital, but simple first aid can concentrate on cooling the burns and treating the patient for shock. Apply cold water to the region of the burn and when the skin has had time to cool, cover with a clean bandage or cloth. Never burst blisters or apply ointments, and do not attempt to remove burned clothing because this will often remove skin as well. The reaction to burning is often as important as the burn itself, and any rings, bracelets, tight belts and other tight items of wear should be removed in case of swelling. Try to keep the patient conscious, giving small drinks of cold water, until specialist help arrives.

The effects of chemicals require specialized treatment, but for corrosive chemicals (see above) large amounts of water should be used to ensure that the material is diluted to an extent that makes it less dangerous. In electronics servicing work, the risk of swallowing poisonous substances is fairly small, and the main risks are of skin contact with corrosive or poisonous materials and the inhalation of poisonous fumes. Remember that common solvents like trichloro-ethylene and carbon tetrachloride degreasing liquids give off toxic fumes; these liquids should be used only under extractor hoods or in other well ventilated situations. Never try to identify a solvent by sniffing at a bottle. Some solvents, like acetone and amyl acetate, are a serious fire hazard in addition to giving off toxic fumes.

Most first aid is concerned with the treatment of minor wounds. The most important first step is to ensure that a wound is clean, washing in water if there is any dirt around or in the wound. Minor bleeding will often stop of its own accord, or a styptic pencil (alum stick) can be used to make the blood clot. More extensive bleeding must be treated by applying pressure and putting on a fairly tight sterile dressing – one dressing can be put over the top of an older one if necessary rather than disturbing a wound. Medical help should always be summoned for severe wounding or loss of blood, because an anti-tetanus injection may be required even if the effects of the wound are not serious.

Test questions

2.1   You find that your waste-paper basket is burning. You should first
      (a) trample out the flames
      (b) call for help

(c) run

(d) use a green extinguisher.

2.2 You find a colleague slumped over a live test-rig. You should first
(a) call for help
(b) apply artificial respiration
(c) switch off the mains supply
(d) dial 999.

2.3 You are called out to repair a TV receiver in a house. Who is primarily responsible for safety?
(a) the government
(b) yourself
(c) the house owner
(d) the insurance company.

2.4 The 3-pin plug on an audio amplifier should have
(a) the green/yellow lead on the earth terminal and a 3A fuse
(b) the brown lead on the earth terminal and a 13A fuse
(c) the blue lead on the earth terminal and a 3A fuse
(d) the green/yellow lead on the earth terminal and a 13A fuse.

2.5 You find a packing-case blocking a workshop doorway. Should you
(a) shift it enough to squeeze around it?
(b) stop using that door?
(c) report it verbally and in the logbook?
(d) paint a yellow line around it?

2.6 A piece of equipment has a chassis that is connected to one pole of the mains supply. You should work on it live only if
(a) the chassis is earthed
(b) the supply comes from an isolating transformer
(c) the chassis is connected to the neutral line
(d) the supply is taken from an isolating transformer and the chassis is earthed.

3   Graphs, waveforms and calculations

Refer to syllabus section 07(007)

Note: The purpose of this chapter is to explain the mathematical methods which are used in electronics generally, but particularly in connection with C & G Course 224.

Students are neither expected nor encouraged to tackle the whole of this chapter in one reading. They would be better advised to tackle each of its topics one at a time, as and when the need for understanding a particular topic arises. Thereafter, constant practice in handling the mathematical techniques involved will soon make their use come as second nature.

Graphs

Throughout this series, graphs will be freely used to present information about electronic components, systems and circuits. It is therefore important for the student to understand both how to plot graphs and how to interpret the information they so conveniently present.

The purpose of a graph is to take the place of a detailed table of measurements in showing at a glance how two quantities are related to one another in differing circumstances. The table of voltages and currents in Table 3.1, for example, lists the results of a series of measurements which have been taken on a given circuit.

Try to guess quickly from this table alone the value of voltage that would result in a current flow of, say, 0.2 A. Then see how much quicker and more

Table 3.1 Voltages and currents

V in volts	I in amps
0.85	0.07
1.9	0.15
3.0	0.24
3.9	0.31
5.4	0.43

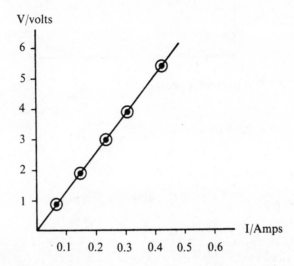

Figure 3.1 A typical linear graph

accurate your estimate would have been if the same information had been shown in the form of the graph which forms Figure 3.1. In this graph, the relationship between the two sets of data is at once obvious, and the closely approximate values of all current flows and their corresponding voltages can be read off from the graph scales at a glance.

To plot such a graph, two scales are needed. One is drawn along what is called the X-axis of the graph. It is the direction which is horizontal when the book you are reading is held upright. This X-axis has marks equally spaced along its length to represent equal steps of (in this particular case) current values.

The other axis, called the Y-axis, is drawn vertically, i.e., at 90°, to the X-axis, and in this case is used to plot values of voltage. Equal spaces along this scale thus represent equal steps of voltage. The two scale axes are shown in Figure 3.2.

To plot the graph line itself, a pair of corresponding values of V (volts) and I (amps) is chosen, and the values of each are located on the appropriate axis. A

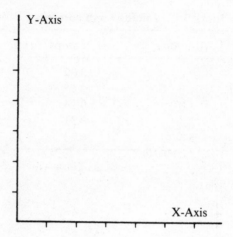

Figure 3.2   The axes of a graph

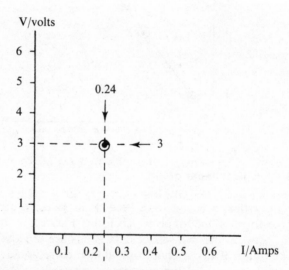

Figure 3.3   Plotting a point from a table of values

light line is then drawn vertically upwards (and so parallel to the Y-axis) from the location of the selected current value on the X-axis, and another light line is drawn horizontally (and so parallel to the X-axis) from the location of the selected voltage value on the Y-axis. Where these two lines meet, a lightly pencilled dot is made to form the first point of the graph, its position representing a pair of values, one of current and one of voltage (see Figure 3.3).

Other pairs of values are then similarly located and plotted to form a set of dots. These are then joined by a firmer line, drawn as smoothly and regularly as

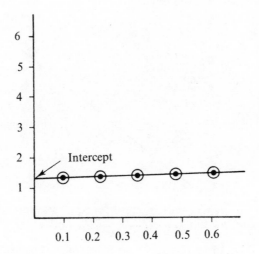

Figure 3.4   A graph with an intercept

possible, and a *graph line* is produced.

When the dots joined in this fashion produce a straight line, the graph (and therefore the relationship between the two values being plotted against one another) is said to be *linear*. A linear graph is of great importance because:

(a)   It can be extended in either direction merely by using a ruler.
(b)   It indicates that one quantity is *directly proportional* to the other.

The example given in Figure 3.1 is a linear graph showing that the voltage across a resistor is proportional to the current flow through the same resistor. This relationship is expressed mathematically in the highly important equation known as Ohm's Law.

Note how the axes are labelled with a symbol, oblique stroke and unit quantity. For example. V/Volts is to be read as 'V, in units of volts', and I/Amps as 'I, in units of amperes'.

The point 0,0 – meaning the point at which both X = 0 and Y = 0 and so the point at which both of the quantities plotted on the graph have zero values – is called the *origin* of the graph. The graph-line in Figure 3.1 passes right through this point, indicating as it does so that there is no voltage across a resistor when no current flows through it.

If, however, a graph were plotted of the voltages across a re-chargeable cell against the current passing through the cell during the charging period (see Figure 3.4), the graph line would again be straight but would *not* pass through the origin, because a voltage undoubtedly exists across the cell even when no charging current is flowing.

A graph like this is said to have an *intercept*. The intercept, in this example, is on the Y-axis, which means that there is a value of Y when X = 0. The *intercept*

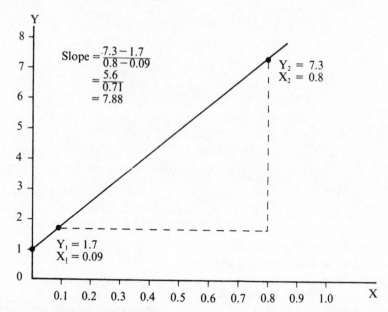

Figure 3.5   The slope of a graph

is this value of Y.

Another quantity that can be read off a linear graph is its *slope*. The slope of a linear graph is found by taking two points, well spaced from one another, on the graph line, and finding their X and Y values. In Figure 3.5 the pairs of points taken are X_1; Y_1 and X_2; Y_2, and their values are as shown on the Figure. The lower value of Y_1 is then subtracted from the higher value Y_2, to give $Y_2 - Y_1$; and the X-values are subtracted in the same way, to give $X_2 - X_1$.

The ratio $\dfrac{Y_2 - Y_1}{X_2 - X_1}$ is the slope of the graph. In Figure 3.5 this slope has a value of 7.88.

Note that the values of X and Y are *always read from the scales marked along each axis*, never from any measurement of distance.

Suppose, now, that the value of the slope (m) and of the intercept (c) are known for any linear graph. The value of Y for any value of X can then be calculated from the formula:

$$Y = mX + c.$$

Example: A graph has a slope value of 5 and an intercept of 2. What is the Y value corresponding to X = 3?
Solution: Substitute the data in the equation: $Y = mX + c$.
Then $Y = (5 \times 3) + 2$
$\qquad\quad = 15 + 2$
$\qquad\quad = 17$

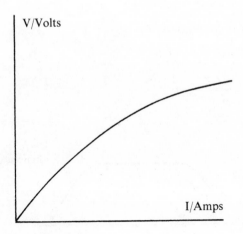

Figure 3.6   A non-linear graph

Note that in the working out of this Example the multiplication was carried out before the addition. It is a general rule that in working out complex equations, all multiplications and divisions are carried out before any additions or subtractions.

Non-linear graphs

Not all graphs are linear. For example, a graph of current plotted against voltage in a component called a thermistor would take the shape shown in Figure 3.6. Such graphs have no single value of slope. They are useful for finding instantaneous values of I and V which lie within the range of the graph line, but the graph line itself cannot be extended except by guesswork.

Sometimes a straight-line graph is obtained by the use of scales which are not themselves linear. A *non-linear scale* is one in which equal distances along the scale do *not* represent equal amounts of the quantity being plotted. The graph in Figure 3.7, for instance, uses a *logarithmic* scale – on which each equal step of distance represents a *tenfold* increase of the quantity being plotted. Logarithmic scales are often used for plotting the frequency of electronic signals, because a very large range of values can then be plotted on a single graph.

One disadvantage of a logarithmic graph is that it is never easy to locate intermediate values lying between the printed values on the axes. For example, the point representing a value of 50 along the X-axis in Figure 3.7 is not midway between 10 and 100 nor midway between 1 and 100. Another disadvantage is that the value of the slope of a logarithmic graph is of little use even if the graph happens to be a straight line.

31

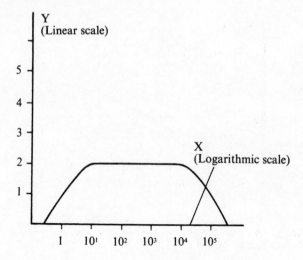

Figure 3.7   A graph with a single logarithmic scale

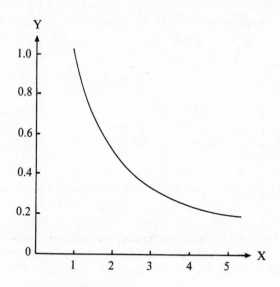

Figure 3.8   An inverse law graph

Inverse law graph

This shape of graph is found when one quantity is related to the *inverse* of another. For example, the inverse of X is $1/X$, so that a graph of $Y = 1/X$ would take the shape illustrated in Figure 3.8.

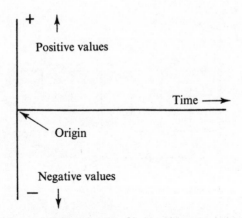

Figure 3.9   Graph axes for the plotting of waveforms

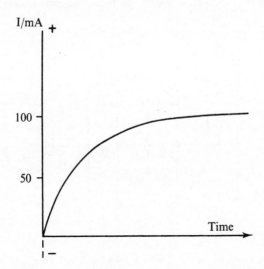

Figure 3.10   An exponential waveform having no negative values

Waveform graphs

In this important type of graph, the quantity plotted along the X-axis is always *time*. The Y-axis is extended below the X-axis in order that positive values can be plotted above the X-axis and negative values below it, as shown in Figure 3.9.

A waveform graph indicates what values of voltage or current are present in a circuit *at different times after the circuit has been switched on*. In Figure 3.10 for instance, the current (which is of course zero before the circuit is switched on) rises gradually to a maximum value of 100 mA after some time. Figure 3.11

33

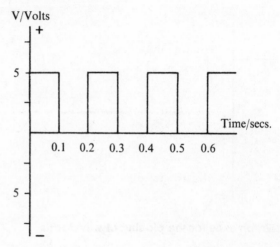

Figure 3.11   Graph of a square wave having no negative values

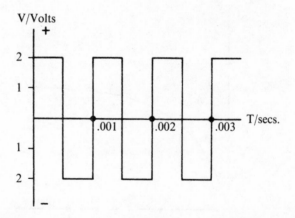

Figure 3.12   Graph of a square wave having both positive and negative values

depicts a voltage which is alternatively switched on and off, forming a type of waveform called a *square wave*.

Figure 3.12 also shows a square wave, but this time the voltage alternates between positive and negative values, with the time taken for a complete cycle of change (the period of the wave) – from positive to negative and back to positive again – only 0.001 seconds. Figure 3.13 illustrates a very common type of waveform called a *sine-wave*, which changes smoothly from positive to negative values and back again to positive, in a time (for the example shown in Figure 3.13) of 0.02 seconds. This time is also called the *period* of the wave. This

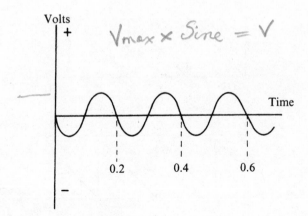

Figure 3.13   Graph of a sine wave

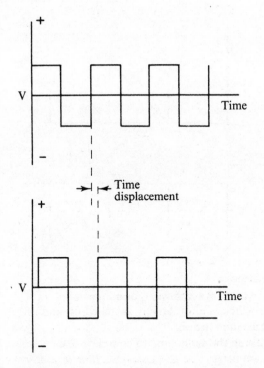

Figure 3.14   Square wave graphs showing time displacement

particular type of sine-wave is typical of the mains (line) supply voltage used in the UK.

Figure 3.14 shows a pair of square waves taken from different parts of a single

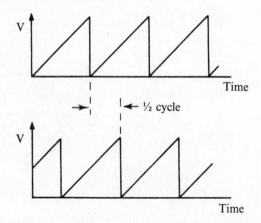

Figure 3.15 Sawtooth waveforms, with half-period displacement

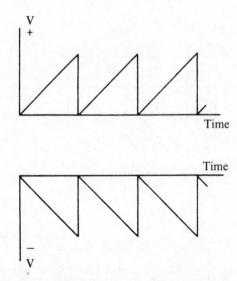

Figure 3.16 Sawtooth waveforms – one inverted

circuit, but plotted together on the same time scale. It will be seen that the waves, though taking the same time to complete one cycle, are not in step with each another. Such waves are said to have a *time displacement* relative to each other.

When the waves are completely out of step – as they are in the so-called *sawtooth* waveforms shown in Figure 3.15 – they are said to be displaced by half of a time period.

Figure 3.16 shows another example of waves which are of the same general

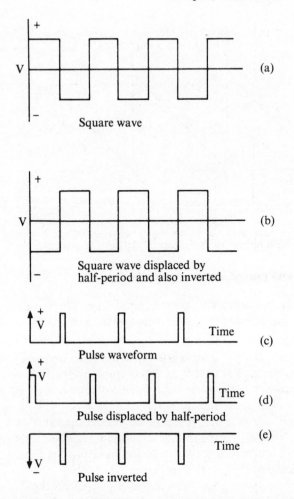

Figure 3.17   Inversion and half-period displacement contrasted

shape, but which are nevertheless not identical. In the case shown, one wave is said to be *inverted* with respect to the other. With waves like sine-waves and square waves, there is no difference in shape between waves which are displaced by a half-period and those which are inverted. For other waveshapes, the differences are both marked and important, as can be seen in Figure 3.17.

Frequency and frequency response

The *frequency* of a wave is defined as the number of complete cycles from positive peak to negative peak and back again (or the reverse), which occur in it

37

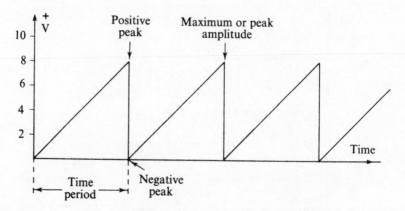

Note: The negative peak need not be an actual negative voltage, but only at a voltage which is negative with respect to the voltage of the positive peak.

Figure 3.18   Time period and peak amplitude

per second. This frequency can be calculated from the waveform graph by reading off the *time period* (T) of one cycle and then calculating (1/T, which is the frequency.

Example: The time period of a wave is 0.05s. What is the frequency of the wave?
Solution: 1/T in this case is 1/0.05, or 20 complete cycles of wave per second. The unit of frequency is the *hertz* (shortened to Hz), so the frequency in the example above would be written as 20 Hz.

The *peak amplitude* of a waveform is the maximum value of the quantity plotted on the Y-axis – be it voltage or current, positive or negative. For example, the amplitude of the voltage in the waveform of Figure 3.11 is 5V, while the amplitude of that plotted in Figure 3.18 is 8V.

In a *frequency response graph*, amplitude is plotted on the Y-axis and frequency on the X-axis, so that the graph can be used to read off the amplitude of a waveform at a number of different frequencies. When such a graph is plotted, it is usual to assume that a circuit such as an amplifier is fed with waveforms having the same amplitude, whatever their frequency. The graph then shows the amplitude of the wave at the output of the circuit at every frequency which has been applied (see Figure 3.19).

A frequency response graph of this kind is an important factor in deciding whether an amplifier is suitable for its planned application.

Denary numbers

A denary number is one which is either a multiple of ten or a fraction having a power of ten as its denominator. Thus the number 100 is a denary number,

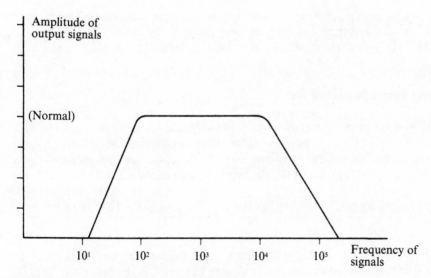

Figure 3.19   A frequency response graph

equal to 10 tens. The number 89 is also a denary number, equal to eight tens plus nine units. The number 0.2 is also a denary number equal to 2/10, a decimal fraction.

Denary numbers can be added, subtracted, multiplied and divided digit by digit, starting with the *least significant* figures (the *units* of a whole number, or the figure *farthest to the right of the decimal point* of a fraction), and then working left towards the *most significant* figures.

Ratios

Many of the quantities used in electronics measurements are *ratios*, such as the ratio of the current (I_c) flowing in the collector circuit of a transistor to the current (I_b) flowing in its base circuit.

A ratio consists of one number divided by another, and can be expressed in several different ways:

(a)   As a common fraction, such as 2/25.
(b)   As a decimal fraction, such as 0.47.
(c)   As a percentage, such as 12% (which is in fact a short way of expressing the fraction 12/100).

To convert a decimal ratio into a percentage, shift the decimal point *two places to the right*, so that 0.47 becomes 47%. If there are empty places, fill them with zeros, so that 0.4 becomes 40%.

To convert a percentage to a decimal ratio, imagine a decimal point where the % sign was, and then shift this point *two places to the left*, so that 12% becomes 0.12. Once again, empty places are filled with zeros, so that 8% becomes 0.08.

Averages and tolerances

The average value of a set of values is found by adding up all the values in the set and then dividing by the number of items comprising the set. Say a set of resistors has the following values: one 7R, two 8R, three 9R, four 10R, four 11R, three 12R, and two 13R, the average value of the set is found as follows:

$$\frac{7+8+8+9+9+9+10+10+10+10+11+11+11+11+12+12+12+13+13}{19} \text{ or } \frac{196}{19}$$

This divides out to 10.32, so that the average value of the set is 10.32R.

Note that such an average value is often not 'real', in the sense that there is in the set no actual resistor having the average value of 10.32R. It is like saying that the average family size in the UK today is 2.2 children. This might indeed be a quite truthful statement – but you will seldom in practice meet a family containing two children and 0.2 of a third one ...

In a manufacturing process, the average value becomes a *target value* – one that it is aimed to achieve – whether it be a value of length, of volume, of electrical resistance or of anything else. When the value of a component turns out to be not equal to the target value, it is said to have a *tolerance*. Thus in a box containing 10R resistors, an 'odd-one-out' resistor which has a measured value of 12R would be said to have 'a tolerance of 2R'.

Tolerances are in practice usually expressed as percentages. Thus 2R/10R expressed as a percentage becomes 2/10 × 100% = 20%, so that the tolerance of the odd resistor is said to be within *20% of the target value*.

Tolerances are usually written as ± percentages, so that a tolerance of '± 20%' means that some samples in a given batch may be as much as '20% high' (+) and others '20% low' (−) compared to the target or average value of the batch as a whole.

Powers of ten: significant figures

Consider the numbers 0.047, 47 and 47 000. Each consists of the two figures 4 and 7, plus a power of ten expressed by zeros inserted either before or after the decimal point (or assumed decimal point). Thus 0.047 is the fraction 47/1000, and 47 000 is 47 × 1000. The figures 4 and 7 are called the *significant figures* of all these numbers, because the zeros before or after them simply indicate a

Table 3.2 Powers of ten in index form

Number	Power	Written as:
1/1 000 000	-6	10^{-6}
1/100 000	-5	10^{-5}
1/10 000	-4	10^{-4}
1/1 000	-3	10^{-3}
1/100	-2	10^{-2}
1/10	-1	10^{-1}
1	0	10^{0}
10	1	10^{1}
100	2	10^{2}
1 000	3	10^{3}
10 000	4	10^{4}
100 000	5	10^{5}
1 000 000	6	10^{6}

power of ten.

Note, by the way, that zero can itself be a significant figure if it lies between two other significant figures – as, for example, in the numbers 407 and 0.407.

For many purposes in electronics, only two significant figures are needed to express the value of a quantity, so that numbers can often be expressed as two figures multiplied by a power of ten, either larger or smaller than unity. Powers of ten are written in index form, as shown in Table 3.2. A *positive index number* indicates a number greater than unity; a *negative index number* indicates a number less than unity. For instance, the number $1.2 \times 10^3 = 1\ 200$, the number $4.7 \times 10^{-2} = 0.047$, and so on.

To avoid having to write the power of ten when electrical units such as volts, amperes or ohms are used, a system of *standard prefixes* has been adopted. Table 3.3 lists some of the more commonly used of these prefixes. Most of them derive from an appropriate Greek or Latin root, and consist of a few letters only.

Two simple examples will suffice to show how the system works. A current flow of 0.015 amperes can be simpler expressed as a current flow of 15mA, which is 15×10^{-3} A. A resistance of 56 000 ohms, which is equal to 56×10^3 ohms, is written 56K (the ohm sign Ω being often omitted).

The British Standard system of marking values of *resistance* (BS1852/1977) differs somewhat from the above, but has considerable advantages, particularly in drawing work. The essence of the system is that the ohm sign Ω is never used, nor is the decimal point. Mistakes caused by an unclear decimal point, or by a spot mark mistaken for a decimal point, are thus eliminated.

Table 3.3 Some standard prefixes

Multiplier	Power	Prefix	Abbreviation
1/1 000 000 000 000	10^{-12}	pico-	p
1/1 000 000 000	10^{-9}	nano-	n
1/1 000 000	10^{-6}	micro-	μ
1/1 000	10^{-3}	milli-	m
1 000	10^{3}	kilo-	K
1 000 000	10^{6}	mega-	M
1 000 000 000	10^{9}	giga-	G
1 000 000 000 000	10^{12}	tera-	T

In this BS system, all values in ohms are indicated by the letter R, all values in kilohms by the *capital* letter K, and all values in megohms by M. These letters are then placed where the decimal point would normally be found, and the latter is thereby eliminated. Thus R47 = 0.47 ohms; 5K6 = 5.6 kilohms; 2M2 = 2.2 megohms.

With the partial exception that both upper-case and lower-case K and k are used to mean the same thing – 'kilohm' – this BS system has been followed throughout this series.

Transposition to algebraic formulae

Algebraic formulae are used in electronics to indicate, briefly but exactly, how quantities such as voltage, current, resistance and others can be related to one another. These formulae can be *transposed* – which means re-expressed in a more convenient, but equally valid, form – according to the ordinary rules of algebra.

The most important of these rules can be (rather informally) expressed in two statements:

(1) You can do anything you find convenient to one side of an equation provided you do exactly the same thing to the other side of it.
(2) You can do anything you find convenient to the dividend of an expression provided you do exactly the same thing to its divisor. (In the mathematical equation 50/5 = 10, '50' is the *dividend*, '5' the *divisor* and '10' the *quotient*).

For example, the very important Ohm's Law formula will be familiar to you as $V = R \times I$. This equation can be validly transposed into another equally convenient form in the following way:

(a) By changing its sides round, so that $R \times I = V$

(b) by dividing both its sides by I, so that $\dfrac{R \times I}{I} = \dfrac{V}{I}$

(c) By realizing that $\dfrac{I}{I} = 1$ and so cannot affect the left-hand side of the equation

if it is cancelled entirely from it, so that $R = \dfrac{V}{I}$

Example: The reactance X_c of a capacitor is given by the equation: $X_c = \dfrac{1}{2\pi f C}$.

Express C in terms of 2, π, f, and X_c.
Solution: Invert both sides of the equation and change them round so that

$X_c = \dfrac{1}{2\pi f C}$ becomes $2\pi f C = \dfrac{1}{X_c}$

Now divide both sides of the new equation by $2\pi f$, so that

$$\frac{2\pi f C}{2\pi f} = \frac{1}{2\pi f X_c}$$

Cancel all quantities which appear in identical form both above and below

the line in the left-hand side of the equation, and $C = \dfrac{1}{2\pi f X_c}$ which is the

transposed formula.
Example: The reactance X_L of an inductor is given by the equation $X_L = 2\pi f L$.
Express L in terms of 2, π, f and X_L.
Solution: Divide both sides of the equation by $2\pi f$, so that

$$\frac{X_L}{2\pi f} = \frac{2\pi f L}{2\pi f}$$

and cancel all quantities that appear both above and below the line, then rearrange as:

$$L = \frac{X_L}{2\pi f}$$

Example: The condition for tuning a circuit containing capacitance and inductance is written as:

$$\frac{1}{2\pi f C} = 2\pi f L.$$

Express f in terms of the other quantities.
Solution: Multiply both sides by $2\pi f$, so that

$$\frac{2\pi f}{2\pi f C} = 2\pi f \times 2\pi f L$$

and then cancel all quantities that appear both above and below the line, and rearrange:

$$\frac{1}{C} = 4\pi^2 f^2 L$$

Now divide by L and rearrange:

$$4\pi^2 f^2 = \frac{1}{LC}$$

divide by $4\pi^2$ to get:

$$f^2 = \frac{1}{4\pi^2} \cdot \frac{1}{LC}$$

and then take the square root of each side:

$$f = \frac{1}{2\pi\sqrt{LC}}$$

Scientific calculators

In the past, tables have been used to help in solving complex calculations, or calculations involving numbers containing many figures. The use of electronic calculators has nowadays made such tables more or less redundant.

To solve the type of calculations encountered in electronics, a scientific calculator, preferably a type that incorporates all or most of the keys shown in Figure 3.20 is a highly convenient tool. Such a calculator, which need not be expensive, will make unnecessary the use of sets of tables for any of the calculations which will need to be made throughout this course.

The following hints on how to use a scientific calculator assume that the calculator in question is of the 'algebraic' type, rather than being one of those rare models which makes use of the so-called *Reverse Polish Notation* (R.P.N.).

For multiplication, division, addition and subtraction, key in the numbers and symbols exactly as in the examples below. The answers will in all cases appear on the display.

⑤ ⊗ ④ ⊜   giving the answer 20
③ ⊝ ② ⊜   giving the answer 1.5
⑦ ⊕ ④ ⊜   giving the answer 11
⑧ ⊖ ⑤ ⊜   giving the answer 3

When a number is written in the form of figures having a power of ten (i.e. in so-called 'scientific notation'), use the EXP or EE key as shown below:

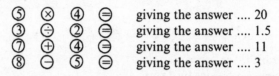

To enter 5.6×10^5, key ⑤ ⊙ ⑥ (EXP) ⑤ ⊜   Answer ....

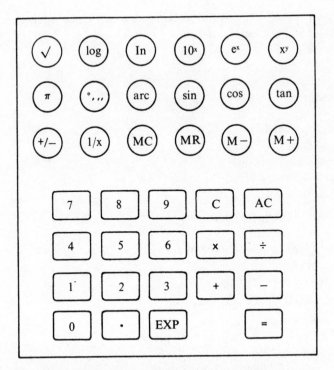

Figure 3.20   A typical scientific calculator keyboard layout

To enter 4.7×10^{-3}, key ④ ⊙ ⑦ (EXP) ③ (+/−) (=)Answer ....

For operations which use the top three rows of keys in Figure 3.20, key in the number first, then the symbol. The answer will appear when the symbol key is pressed. There is no need to press the (=) key at all. Examples:

To find $\sqrt{5}$ (the square root of 5), key ⑤ (√) . The answer appears as 2.236.

To find log 18 (the logarithm of 18), key ① ⑧ (log) . The answer appears as 1.2552.

To find 1/27 (the inverse of 27), key ② ⑦ (1/x) . The answer appears as 0.037.

To find sin 27° (the sine of 27 degrees), key ② ⑦ (sin) . The answer appears as 0.4539.

Note: The answers given above have been rounded off.

When problems involving angles need to be solved, it may be necessary to set

45

a switch on the calculator to the correct units for measuring angles. In all the problems set in this series, the units in which angles are measured will be *degrees*.

Test questions

3.1   In the number 537, the digit 7 is
(a) a binary digit
(b) the least-significant digit
(c) the most-significant digit
(d) a decimal fraction.

3.2   A linear graph is one that
(a) represents a sine wave
(b) represents the length of some quantity
(c) is a straight line
(d) is plotted on a logarithmic scale.

3.3   A point on a graph represents
(a) voltage or current
(b) the distance from the origin of the graph
(c) the length of some quantity
(d) a relationship between two quantities.

3.4   What quantity relating to a set of waveforms might be measured in microseconds?
(a) phase difference
(b) amplitude
(c) shape
(d) frequency.

3.5   A logarithmic scale would be used when
(a) one graphed quantity is a power
(b) both positive and negative values need to be shown
(c) waveforms are being plotted
(d) one graphed quantity has a very wide range of values.

3.6   The prefix M means
(a) one hundred
(b) one thousand
(c) ten thousand
(d) one million.

4 Electrical units and measurements

Refer to syllabus section 06 (6.1 to 6.9)

In the construction of electronic circuits and components, *conductors* are materials which allow electric current to flow through them, and which can therefore form part of a circuit in which a steady current flows. Most metals are conductors. Gases at low pressure (as in neon tubes) and solutions of salts, acids or alkalis in water will also conduct electricity.

Insulators are materials which do not permit a steady electric current to flow through them and which are therefore used to hinder or prevent such a flow. Insulators are predominantly non-metallic in character. Natural insulators, such as sulphur and pitch, are no longer used; and plastic materials like polystyrene and polythene have largely taken their place.

A good example of the contrasting uses of insulators and conductors is to be found in the boards used to make the framework on which printed circuits are built. The boards are made of a stiff bonded paper called 'SRBP' which is impregnated with a plastic resin (the name 'SRBP' stands for 'synthetic resin bonded paper'); but the conducting tracks on the boards are made of copper or from metallic inks.

Both *insulation* and *conduction* are relative terms. A conductor which can pass very small currents may not conduct nearly well enough to be used with large currents. An insulator which is sufficient for a torch cell would be dangerously inadequate when faced with the voltage of the mains (line) supply.

The fitness for their purpose of both 'good' and 'bad' conductors and insulators is assessed by measuring their *resistance*. The resistance of any sample of a substance is a measure of the degree of opposition it presents to the flow of an electric current. A small area of any material will have more resistance than a large area of the same material. A long strip of the material has more resistance than a short strip of the same material.

The resistance of a sample of a given substance therefore depends on its dimensions. In formula:

$$R \propto \frac{L}{A}$$

where *L* represents the length of the sample and *A* its cross-sectional area. The sign $\propto$ means 'is proportional to'.

The formula therefore reads in full as: *Resistance is proportional to sample length divided by the sample's area of cross-section.*

Resistance is measured in units called *ohms* (symbol Ω), which will be defined shortly.

Example: A wire 2 metres long possesses a resistance of 5 ohms. What would be the resistance of a 1.5m sample of the same wire?

Solution: If a 2m sample has a resistance of 5 ohms, the resistance of a 1m sample must be $5/2 = 2.5$ ohms. A 1.5 metre length will therefore have a resistance of $2.5 \times 1.5 = 3.75$ ohms.

Example: A sample of wire of radius 0.2 mm has a resistance of 12 ohms. What would be the resistance of a sample of the same material of the same length but having a 0.3 mm radius.

Solution: The area of a cross-section is proportional to the square of the

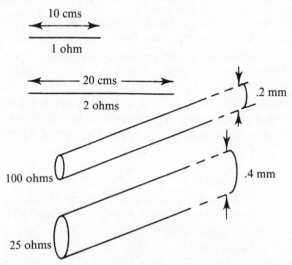

Figure 4.1   Both wire length and wire diameter affect resistance

radius. Therefore Resistance $A \times$ Radius $A^2 =$ Resistance $B \times$ Radius B^2. Substitute the data, and simplify

$$12 \times .2^2 = R \times .3^2$$
$$\therefore R = \frac{12 \times .2^2}{.3^2} = \frac{12 \times 2^2}{3^2}$$
$$\therefore R = \frac{12 \times 4}{9} = \frac{16}{3} \text{ or } 5\frac{1}{3} \text{ ohms.}$$

The resistance value of a sample of material does not depend only on its dimensions, however, because every material has a different value of resistance per standard sample. This resistance per standard sample is called the *resistivity* of the material in question. It is measured in units called *ohm-metres* (written as Ωm). The resistance of a sample of any material is then given by the formula:

$$R = \frac{\rho \times L}{A}$$

where ρ (the Greek letter 'rho') represents the resistivity of the material. *Example*: Copper has value of resistivity equal to $1.7 \times 10^{-8}\Omega$m. What is the resistance of 12m of copper wire of 0.3 mm radius?

Solution: Substitute the data in the equation $R = \frac{\rho.L}{A}$, putting all lengths into metres and recalling that $A = \pi r^2$,

Then,
$$R = \frac{1.7 \times 10^{-8} \times 12}{\pi \times (.0003)^2}$$
$$= \frac{20.4 \times 10^{-8}}{2.83 \times 10^{-7}} = 0.72\Omega.$$

The resistivity values of some common materials are listed in Table 4.1.

The material listed earlier as manganin is a copper-based alloy containing manganese and nickel, much used in the construction of wire-bound resistors. P.T.F.E. is the high-resistivity plastic material polytetrafluoroethylene.

Resistors

Resistors are components possessing a stated value of resistance. Methods of construction include wire-wound, carbon-moulded, carbon film and metal film resistors.

Wire-wound resistors are constructed from lengths of wire, often a nickel-chromium alloy, and are used when comparatively low values of resistance are

Table 4.1 Approximate resistivity values of some common insulators and conductors

Material	Resistivity (expressed in units of 10^{-8}ohm-metres)
Aluminium	2.7
Copper	1.7
Iron	10.5
Mercury	96
Manganin	43
Bakelite	10^5
Glass	10^{12}
Quartz	10^{20}
P.T.F.E.	10^{20}

Figure 4.2 Alternative resistor symbols

required. They are particularly useful when the resistor may become very hot in use, or when precise resistance values are needed. *Moulded carbon resistors* are cheap to manufacture but cannot be made to precise values of resistance. Their large tolerances mean that the values of individual resistors have to be measured and suitable ones selected if a precise value of resistance is needed. *Carbon* and *metal film resistors* are made, as the name suggests, from thin films of conducting material. They can be manufactured in quantity batches, but to fairly precise values.

Two symbols for a resistor in a circuit are shown in Figure 4.2. The older zig-zag symbol is still used, particularly in the USA but both are British Standard symbols. Values of resistance are given in ohms (Ω). In circuit diagrams, they are coded R for 'ohms', K (officially) or k (very commonly, even in this series) for 'kilohms' (thousands of ohms), and M for 'megohms', or millions of ohms. The letters R, K, or M are placed in the position of the decimal point when a resistance value is written against the resistor symbol, as was explained in Chapter 3.

Table 4.2   20% and 10% tolerance preferred values

20%	10%
1.0	1.0
	1.2
1.5	1.5
	1.8
2.2	2.2
	2.7
3.3	3.3
	3.9
4.7	4.7
	5.6
6.8	6.8
	8.2

Resistors are manufactured with certain average values aimed at. These values are called *preferred values*. They are chosen so that no resistor, whatever its actual value of resistance, can possibly lie outside the range of all tolerances. Table 4.2 for instance, lists the 20 per cent and 10 per cent tolerance preferred values.

The above figures are used for all resistor values of a given tolerance range. Values of 2R2, 3K3, 47K, 100K, 1M5 could thus lie in either range; but values of 1R2, 180R, 2K7, 39K, 560K could lie only in the 10 per cent (or closer) tolerance range.

Take a 2K2 resistor in the 20 per cent series. It could have a value of 2k2 ± 20% – that is to say, a range from 2k64 to 1k76. But if such a resistor has a measured value of 2k7 or 1k6, it would not for that reason become a reject. The reason is that the next larger preferred value is 3k3 – and 3.3 − 20 per cent is 2k64. So the 2k7 resistor would quite legitimately be reclassified as a 3k3.

Similarly on the 'down' side. The next value down from 2k2 is 1k5, and 1k5 + 20 per cent is 1k8. A resistor with a measured value of 1k6 would therefore be acceptable as a 1k5.

In other words, the preferred values are so chosen that no resistor made becomes a reject by reason *only* of its measured value.

The preferred value of a resistor is either printed on the resistor or else coded on it by reference to the colour code illustrated and explained below.

In the resistor pictured in Figure 4.3, all the colour bands are printed towards one of its ends. In Figure 4.3a the first band (the one nearest the end itself) represents the first figure of the coded value; the second band represents the second figure; and the third band the number of zeros following this second figure. Thus three bands painted in the sequence, beginning from the

51

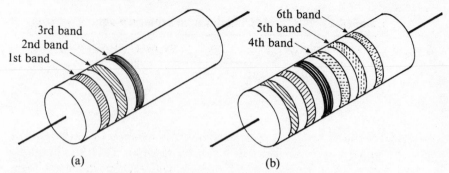

Figure 4.3   Resistor colour coding

Table 4.3   Six-band colour codes

Colour	Significant figure (3)	Multiplier	Tolerance (%)	Temperature coefficient
Silver		0.01	10	
Gold		0.1	5	
Black	0	1		
Brown	1	10	1	100 ppm
Red	2	100	2	50 ppm
Orange	3	1k		15 ppm
Yellow	4	10k		25 ppm
Green	5	100k	0.5	
Blue	6	1M	0.25	
Violet	7	10M	0.1	
Grey	8			
White	9			

end of the resistor – blue, grey, red – would signify (see Table 4.3) a resistor having a preferred value of: 6-8-two zeros, or 6800 ohms. Such a resistor would in practice always be described as a 'a 6k8'.

This colour coding concept can be further extended. A fourth band may be added to indicate the component tolerance. No fourth band signifies ± 20 per cent, whilst a gold or silver band indicates ± 5 per cent or ± 10 per cent respectively. Up to six bands may be used as shown in Figure 4.3(b). Here the first three bands are used to represent significant figures whilst the fourth band indicates the multiplier or number of following zeros. Bands five and six then indicate component tolerance and temperature coefficient respectively.

Moulded-carbon resistors are usually colour-coded. Wire-wound and film-type resistors generally have the resistance value printed on them, using the R,

Table 4.4   Preferred value significant figures for various tolerances

5%	10	11	12	13	15	16	18	20	22	24	27	30	33	36	39	43	47	51	56	62	68	75	82	91
10%	10		12		15		18		22		27		33		39		47		56		68		82	
20%	10				15				22				33				47				68			

K, M notation.

When a resistor is being selected, not only its resistance value but also its *power dissipation* must be considered. A resistor rated at ¼W runs noticeably hot when it is asked to dissipate power of ¼W; and it will be damaged if it is expected to dissipate more power than that. In electronic circuits, most resistors have to dissipate considerably less than ¼W, so that ¼W or even ⅛W types can be used. Component lists therefore specify only those few resistors with higher ratings. The description: '2k2 WW 5W', for example, means '2200-ohm resistance, wire-wound, 5W dissipation'.

For calculations of how power is dissipated in watts, see later in this chapter.

When resistors fail, they commonly become o/c, rarely s/c or they may change their value. This change of value may be either upwards or downwards, and a faulty resistor behaving in this way is said to have 'gone high' or 'gone low'.

The preferred value significant figures for various tolerances are as shown in Table 4.4.

Temperature coefficient

The effect of a change of temperature on a resistor is to change its value of resistance. This change is caused by alteration of the resistivity value of the resistor material rather than by the very small change of dimensions (length and cross-sectional area) which also takes place.

This effect of temperature on resistance is measured by what is called the *temperature coefficient of resistance*, which is defined as the fractional change of resistance per degree of temperature change.

Temperature coefficients may be either positive or negative. A *positive* temperature coefficient means that the resistance value of a resistor at high temperature is *greater* than its resistance value at low temperatures. A *negative* temperature coefficient means that the resistance value at high temperatures is lower than its resistance value at low temperatures.

For example, if a resistor is quoted as having a temperature coefficient of +250 ppm/°C, this means a change of 250 units for each million units of resistance for each degree Celsius of temperature *rise*.

For a 100K resistor raised in temperature from 20°C to 140°C (a change of

120°C), this means:

$$\frac{250}{1\,000\,000} \times 100\,000 \times 120 = 3000\Omega, \text{ or } 3K$$

making the value a total of 103K at the higher temperature.

Taking another example, if an insulator has a resistance of 100M at 20°C and has a temperature coefficient of -500 ppm/°C, then at 200°C (a rise of 180°C) its resistance will drop by:

$$\frac{500}{1\,000\,000} \times 100\,000\,000 \times 180 = 9\,000\,000 \text{ or } 9M$$

so that the resistance at 200° is 91M.

Materials widely used in resistor manufacture normally have positive coefficients of small value. Insulating materials, on the other hand, generally have negative temperature coefficients, and insulation becomes less effective at high temperature.

Electrical units

Electric current consists of the flow of electrons from negative to positive in a circuit. Its rate of flow is measured in *amperes* – abbreviated either 'amps' or 'A'. One ampere is the amount of electric charge, in *coulombs*, which passes a given point in a circuit per second. The coulomb has a value of about 6.289 × 10^{18} electrons.

The measurement of current is done, not by actually counting these millions of millions of millions of electric charges, but by measuring the amount of force exerted between a magnet and the wire carrying the current which is being measured.

The ampere is a fairly large unit, and for most electronics purposes the smaller units *milliamp* (one thousandth of an ampere) and *microamp* (one millionth of an ampere) are more generally used. The abbreviations for these qualities are mA and µA respectively.

In the same way as a pressure is needed to cause a flow of water through a pipe, so an electrical pressure known as *electromotive force* (more commonly, but less accurately, called a *voltage*) is needed to push a current through a resistance. Electromotive force (e.m.f.) is measured in *volts*. A voltage is always present when a current is flowing through a resistance, and the three quantities of volts, amps and ohms are specifically inter-related.

This inter-relationship is known as Ohm's Law, which is mathematically written as V = R × I. In words, it means that *the voltage measured across a given resistor (in volts) is equal to the value of the resistance (in ohms) multiplied by the amount of current flowing (in amperes).*

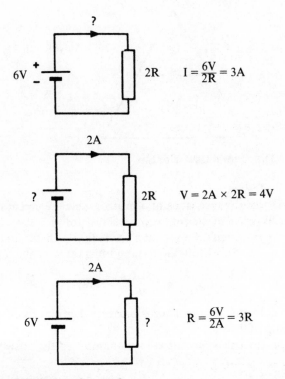

$$I = \frac{6V}{2R} = 3A$$

$$V = 2A \times 2R = 4V$$

$$R = \frac{6V}{2A} = 3R$$

Figure 4.4   How Ohm's Law is used

The Ohm's Law equation can be equally validly rearranged as either R = V/I (resistance equals volts divided by current) or I = V/R (current equals volts divided by resistance).

These equations are the most fundamentally important ones you will meet in all your work on electricity and electronics. In electrical circuits the units in which the law has been quoted – volts, amperes, ohms – should normally always be used; but in electronic circuits it is in practice much easier to measure resistance in K and current in mA. Ohm's Law can be used in any of its forms when both R and I are expressed in these latter units, but the unit of voltage remains always the volt.

There are, therefore, two different combinations of units with which you can use Ohm's Law as it stands:

either: VOLTS – AMPERES – OHMS
or   VOLTS — MILLIAMPERES — KILOHMS

Note: Never mix the two sets of units. To use milliamperes with ohms, or amperes with kilohms, will lead you straight to disaster.

Figure 4.4 illustrates how Ohm's Law is used. Four somewhat more com-

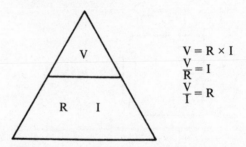

$$V = R \times I$$
$$\frac{V}{R} = I$$
$$\frac{V}{I} = R$$

Figure 4.5   The Ohm's Law triangle

plex examples follow.

Example: What is the resistance of a resistor when a current of 0.1A causes a voltage of 2.5V to be measured across the resistor?

Solution: Express Ohm's Law in the form in which the unknown factor is isolated: R = V/I. Substitute the data in units of volts and amperes.

$$R = \frac{2.5}{0.1} = 25R.$$

Example: What value of resistance is present when a current of 1.4 mA causes a voltage drop of 7.5V?

Solution: The current is measured in milliamps, so the answer will appear in kilohms.

$$R = \frac{V}{I} = \frac{7.5}{1.4} = 5.36 \text{ kilohms, or about 5k4.}$$

Example: What current flows when a 6k8 resistor has a voltage of 1.2V across its terminals?

Solution: The data are already in workable units, so substitute in I = V/R

$$\text{Then } I = \frac{1.2}{6.8} \text{ A} = 0.176\text{A, or } 176 \text{ mA.}$$

Example: What current flows when a 4k7 resistor has a voltage of 9V across its terminals?

Solution: With the value of the resistor quoted in kilohms, the answer will appear in milliamps. So substitute in I = V/R, and

$$I = \frac{9}{4.7} = 0.001915\text{A} = 1.915 \text{ mA.}$$

The importance of Ohm's Law lies in the fact that if only two of the three quantities – current, voltage and resistance – are known, the third of them can always be calculated by using the formula.

The important thing is to remember which way up Ohm's Law reads. Draw the triangle shown in Figure 4.5. Put V at its Vertex, and I and R down below –

and you will never forget it. The formulae follow from this arrangement automatically using a *cover-up* procedure. Place a finger over I and V/R is left, thus I = V/R. The other ratios can be found in a similar way.

Power

When a current flows through a resistor, electrical energy is converted into heat energy, and this heat is passed on to the air around the resistor, and *dissipated*. The rate at which heat is dissipated is called *power*, and is measured in *watts*.

The amount of power dissipated can be calculated from any two of the quantities V (in volts), I (in amps) and R (in ohms), as follows:

(a) Using V and I   Power = V × I watts
(b) Using V and R   Power = V²/R watts
(c) Using I and R   Power = I²R watts

Most electronic circuits use small currents measured in mA, and large values of resistance measured in K. The power dissipated by a resistor is therefore often more conveniently measured in milliwatts. Expressing the units V in volts, I in milliamps and W in milliwatts, the equations to remember become:

The milliwatts dissipated = V^2/R (volts and K)
The milliwatts dissipated = I^2R (milliamps and K)

Example: How much power is dissipated when:
(a) 6V passes a current of 1.4A, (b) 8V is placed across 4 ohms, (c) 0.1A flows through 15R?

Solution:
  (a) Using V × I   Power = 6 × 1.4 = 8.4W
  (b) Using V²/R

$$Power = \frac{8^2}{4} = \frac{64}{4} = 16W$$

  (c) Using I²R   Power = 0.1² × 15 = .01 × 15 = 0.15W

Example: How much power is dissipated when:
(a) 9V passes a current of 50 mA?
(b) 20V is across a 6K8 resistor?
(c) 8 mA flows through a 1K5 resistor?

Solution:
  (a) Using V × I   Power = 9 × 50 = 450 mW
  (b) Using V²/R

$$Power = \frac{20^2}{6.8} = \frac{400}{6.8} = 58.8 \text{ mW}$$

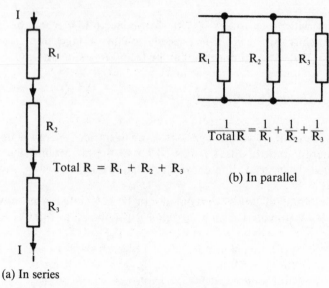

$$\text{Total R} = R_1 + R_2 + R_3$$

(a) In series

$$\frac{1}{\text{Total R}} = \frac{1}{R_1} + \frac{1}{R_2} + \frac{1}{R_3}$$

(b) In parallel

Figure 4.6   Resistors (a) In series; (b) In parallel

(c) Using I^2R $\qquad$ Power $= 8^2 \times 1.5 = 64 \times 1.5 = 96\,\text{mW}$

The amount of energy which is dissipated in the manner described is measured in *joules*. The watt is a *rate* of dissipation equal to the energy loss of one joule per second, so that joules = watts × seconds or watts = joules/seconds. It is found by multiplying the value of power dissipation by the amount of time during which the dissipation continues. The resulting equations are:

Energy dissipated $= V \times I \times t$ joules

$\qquad\qquad\qquad = V^2 t/R$ joules

$\qquad\qquad\qquad = I^2 Rt$ joules

where t is the time during which power dissipation continues, measured in seconds.

Electrical components and appliances are rated according to the power which they dissipate or convert. A 3W resistor, for example, will dissipate 3 joules of energy per second; a 3 kW motor will convert 3000 joules of energy per second into motion (if it is 100 per cent efficient).

As a general rule, the greater the power dissipation required, the larger the component needs to be.

Resistors in series and parallel

Resistors can be connected either in series or in parallel, or in any combination of series and parallel.

When resistors are connected in series (see Figure 4.6(a)), the same current must flow through each in turn. The *total* resistance encountered by the current is therefore the sum of all their values.

When resistors are connected in parallel (Figure 4.6(b)), current flow is divided among the resistors according to their values, with the most current flowing through the lowest-value resistor(s). The same *voltage*, however, is maintained across all the resistors.

Any combination of resistors in series and parallel is capable of being broken down into a single resistance *of equivalent value*. These single resistances are then combined by using the formulae given in Figure 4.6, until a single resistance equivalent in value to the resistance of the combination as a whole is achieved.

It has been said that the equivalent value of resistors *in series* is simply the sum of the resistance values in the series. For example, the equivalent value of 6k8 + 3k3 + 2k2 connected in series is 6.8 + 3.3 + 2.2 = 12.3k, or 12k3. The equivalent resistance of the series is thus greater than is the value of any of the single resistors.

The equivalent value for resistors connected *in parallel* is rather more difficult to calculate. The rule is to calculate the *inverse* (1/R) of the value of every resistor connected in parallel, to *add* all the inverses together, and then to *invert* the result. In formula (as stated in Figure 4.6) $1/R = 1/R_1 + 1/R_2 + 1/R_3$ ... for however many resistors there may be in the parallel combination. For two resistors this can be simplified to:

$$\frac{\text{Product}}{\text{Sum}}, \text{ i.e. } \frac{R_1 R_2}{R_1 + R_2}$$

Example: Find the equivalent resistance of 2k2, 3k3, 6k8 connected in parallel.

Solution:

$$\frac{1}{R} = \frac{1}{2.2} + \frac{1}{3.3} + \frac{1}{6.8}$$
$$= 0.4545 + 0.3030 + 1470$$
$$= 0.9046$$

$$\therefore R = \frac{1}{0.9046} = 1.1054k, \text{ or } 1105.4 \text{ ohms.}$$

The steps needed to solve the above problem on a pocket calculator are:

| 2.2 | | 1/x | | + | | 3.3 | | 1/x | | + | | 6.8 | | 1/x | | = | | 1/x |

When a circuit contains resistors connected both in series and in parallel, the calculations must be carried out in sequence. Figure 4.7 presents two circuits whose total equivalent resistance needs to be found. The procedure is set out below.

In the circuit of Figure 4.7(a), the value of the parallel resistors is calculated first. 10k and 15k combine as follows:

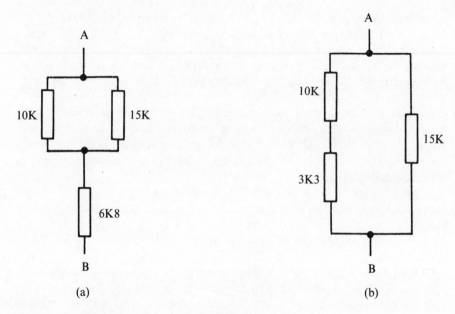

Figure 4.7   Solving series–parallel circuits

$$\frac{1}{R} = \frac{1}{10} + \frac{1}{15} = 0.166$$

$\therefore$ R = 6k (units of k having been used throughout).

This 6k is now added to the 6k8 series-connected resistor to give a total equivalent resistance of 12k8.

In Figure 4.7(b), the series resistance values are combined first. 10k *plus* 3k3 gives 13k3, and this value is now combined in parallel with 15k.

$$\frac{1}{R} = \frac{1}{13.3} + \frac{1}{15} = 0.1418$$
$$\therefore \ R = 7.05k \text{ or } 7k05$$

Note that both series and parallel combinations of resistors can produce values of total resistance which are unobtainable within the normal series of preferred values. This can often be useful.

A highly important circuit using two resistors connected in series is the *potential divider* circuit illustrated in Figure 4.8. The total resistance is $R_1 + R_2$ – which in the example shown is 5k5. By Ohm's Law, current flow must be

$$\frac{V}{R_1 + R_2} = \frac{10}{5.5} = 1.8182 \text{ mA.}$$

Such a current flowing through R_2 requires voltage V which, by Ohm's Law

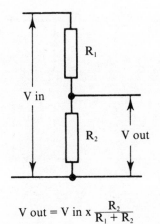
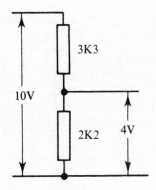

$$V \text{ out} = V \text{ in } x \frac{R_2}{R_1 + R_2}$$

Figure 4.8   The potential divider circuit

again, must be I × R₂. Substitute the known values of current and resistance, and the voltage across R_2 works out at 1.8182 mA × 2k2, or about 4V in the example shown.

A potential divider (or *attenuator*) circuit is used to obtain a lower voltage from a source of high voltage. Where E is the high voltage and V the lower voltage, the lower voltage can be calculated by using the formula:

$$V = \frac{ER_2}{R_1 + R_2}$$

For example, if 10V is applied across a series circuit of 2K and 3K resistors, the voltage across the 3K resistor is:

$$\frac{10 \times 3}{3 + 2} = 6V.$$

Example: Given the circuit shown in Figure 4.9(a), calculate V_{out}, I_1, I_2 and I_3.

Solution: Start with the parallel, equal 20K resistors. Use either the product/ sum rule or recognize that two equal parallel resistors have a value equal to half that of one, so that the circuit becomes that shown in Figure 4.9(b). The total resistance is therefore 10K + 8K = 18K. 18 volts across 18K will cause a total current I_1 = 1 mA. This current through 10K will produce a V_{out} = 10 volts. Now this is the voltage across both 20K resistors, so that I_1 and I_2 are both equal to 10/20K = 0.5 mA.

Measuring instruments

Electrical quantities are measured by instruments such as *multimeters* and *oscilloscopes*. A multimeter (or multi-range meter) is an instrument capable of

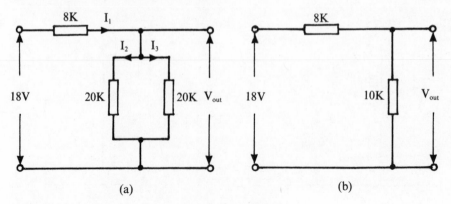

Figure 4.9   A further series–parallel problem

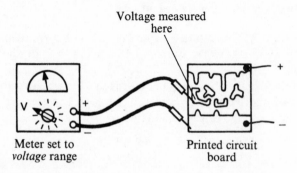

Figure 4.10   Measuring voltage on a printed circuit board

indicating the values of several ranges of currents, voltages and resistances by measuring the current flowing through the meter.

Measurements are made as follows (starting with the circuit switched OFF):

1.   *To measure a voltage*, the leads of the multiplier are clipped to the points across which the voltage is to be measured. One of these points will often be either the chassis, earth or the negative supply line. The multimeter is then switched to the correct range of voltage, and the circuit is switched on. The voltage is then read from the correct scale. See Figure 4.10.

2.   *To read current flow*, the circuit is broken at the place where the current is to be measured. The multimeter leads are then clipped on, one to each side of the circuit break. The meter is set to a suitable range of current flows, and the circuit is switched on. Current value is then read from the correct scale. See Figure 4.11.

Note that, for measurements of either voltage or current, the meter must be connected *in the correct polarity*, with the + (usually red) lead of the meter connected to a more positive voltage.

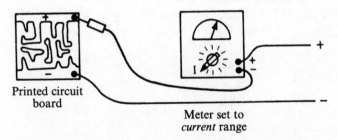

Figure 4.11 Measuring current flow on a printed circuit board

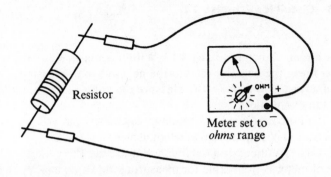

Figure 4.12 Measuring resistance

3. *To read resistances*, the multimeter leads are first short-circuited. The meter is switched to the 'ohms' range, and the set zero adjuster is used to locate the needle pointer over the zero-ohms mark. The leads are then re-connected across the resistor to be measured, and its resistance is read off the scale. See Figure 4.12.

If there is any doubt as to what sort of values of voltage or current will be encountered, *the highest likely range of each* must first be tried on the multimeter. The range switch is then used to select a lower range of values, until a range is found which gives a reading which is *not too near either end of the scale*.

Multimeters always draw current from the circuit under test, so the values of voltage or current which are measured when the meter is connected are not necessarily the same as those which exist when the meter is not connected. To overcome this problem (which is caused by the comparatively low resistance of the multimeter), *electronic voltmeters* can be used. These instruments have very high resistance and so draw very little current from a circuit. They should always be used when measurements have to be taken on high-resistance circuits.

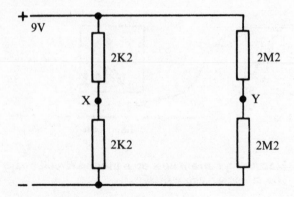

Figure 4.13   Circuit for Exercise 4.1

Exercise 4.1

Connect the circuit shown in Figure 4.13. With the multimeter switched to the 10V scale, connect the negative lead to the negative line. Measure the supply voltage, and adjust it to exactly 9V. Measure the voltages at points X and Y, and record the two values.

Now use the potential divider formula to calculate what voltages would be present at X and at Y if no meter were connected.

If an electronic voltmeter is available, use it to read the voltage at point Y. Which type of meter is preferable for measuring the voltage at Y, and why?

Examples: These examples should be solved by *mental arithmetic* – you can use a calculator to check your answers if necessary. In each question, two quantities are given and you should calculate the third.

V = 9V	V = 6.6V	V = ? 30	V = 27V	V = 12V	V = ? 6.6
R = 18K	R = ?3.300	R = 10K	R = 1K8	R = ?3000	R = 2K2
I = ? .0005	I = 2mA	I = 3mA	I = ? 15m/A	I = 4mA	I = 3mA

Insulation testers are used to measure the very high resistances of insulators. Testers such as the well-known 'Megger' (which is incidentally a registered trade name, but which is nevertheless widely used generically) operate by generating a known high voltage and applying it through a current meter to the insulator under test. Any current flowing through the insulator causes the meter needle to deflect, and the scale indicates the resistance value of the insulator in megohms. Typical proof test voltages are 250V or 500V dc and 500V ac.

Cathode ray oscilloscopes use cathode ray tubes (see Chapter 14) to trace out the waveform of a signal input. A measuring graticule (taking in this case, the form of a transparent scale) enables the dimensions of the signal waveform to be measured. These dimensions can then be converted into voltage and time units by using the conversions marked on the range switches. In use, the CRO

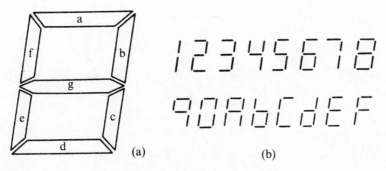

Figure 4.14 The seven-segment display

is connected like a voltmeter.

Signal generators are used to supply signal waveforms, usually sine or square waves at various frequencies. AF (audio frequency) signal generators have outputs whose frequency range is from about 10 Hz to 20 kHz, usually possessing enough power to drive a small loudspeaker. RF (radio frequency) signal generators work at high frequencies, typically 100 kHz to many MHz, and have both low amplitude and low power.

Measuring instruments such as these are used to test components and circuits. The multimeter can test resistance values and check that the correct currents and voltage levels exist in a circuit. Electronic voltmeters are used to test high-resistance circuits. The CRO is an extremely useful instrument which enables the engineer to see the shape, as well as to measure the amplitude and period, of a waveform. In circuits which amplify signals, signal generators provide a signal input which can then be traced through the circuit using the CRO.

A seven-segment readout is now much used in electronic instruments of the digital type to enable readings of voltage, current or resistance to be displayed directly in figures. The basic display consists of seven segments arranged in the form of a figure '8' (see Figure 4.14(a)). Each of the segments *a, b, c, d, e, f* and *g*, can be lit up to distinguish it from its background, so that the figures 0–9 (as well as a few letters of the alphabet) can be displayed by illuminating different segments (Figure 4.14(b)).

Seven-segment readouts need to be driven by a *decoder* circuit (generally taking the form of an integrated circuit) so that the correct segments are illuminated from the appropriate number input to the decoder.

Test questions

4.1   Generally a circuit has to be broken to measure
      (a) insulation

(b) voltage
(c) current
(d) power

4.2 When a potential difference of 6 volts exists across a 1kΩ resistor, the current flowing will be
(a) 6mA
(b) 3 A
(c) 0.16 A
(d) 1/6 mA

4.3 The unit of resistivity is the
(a) ohm
(b) ohm metre
(c) ohm per metre
(d) metre

4.4 Which of the following has the highest resistivity?
(a) aluminium
(b) P.T.F.E.
(c) wood
(d) mercury

4.5 In the resistor colour code, the third band represents the
(a) first significant figure
(b) second significant figure
(c) tolerance
(d) number of zeros.

4.6 Two strips of the same metal A and B have the same lengths and thicknesses but A is half the width of B. The resistance ratio A to B is
(a) 4:1
(b) 2:1
(c) 1:4
(d) 1:2

Exercise 4.2
Measure the resistance of a selection of resistors, and compare your readings with the marked values. Use either a multimeter or a resistance bridge for measurement.

Exercise 4.3
Measure the insulation resistance of unpopulated PCBs and cables. Use a Megger or equivalent on the 1000 M range, and make sure that a selected PCB is clean and dry. Place the PCB (or stripboard) on an insulator, such as polystyrene foam, and connect the two leads from the Megger to different

tracks on the PCB or stripboard. Switch on the Megger and read the insulation resistance.

Now coil a length of television coaxial cable on to the polystyrene foam, and make certain that the inner and output conductors are well separated at the ends of the cable. Connect one of the Megger leads to the inner conductor of the cable and the other lead to the outer conductor. Switch on the Megger and measure the insulation resistance for the cable. Repeat this on a section of mains cable, and on a stereo amplifier connection cable.

5   Circuits, components and construction

Refer to syllabus section 03 (3.1 and 3.2)

An electrical circuit consists of a source of voltage, often called the *supply*, or *generator*; the *load*, which has resistance and which dissipates heat; and *conductors* which connect the supply to the load. See Figure 5.1. In addition, *switches* are used to interrupt or to restore the flow of current, and *fuses* are put in to protect the circuit against the over-heating and risk of fire which would result from the excessive current which could flow if the circuit were faulty.

Any supply or generator requires at least two terminals connected to the load.

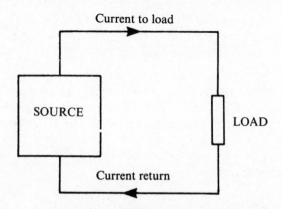

Figure 5.1   Source and load in an electrical circuit

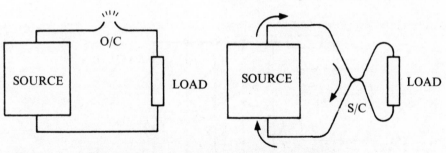

Figure 5.2   Open-circuit (o/c) and short-circuit (s/c) faults

Current in a d.c. circuit flows out of the supply or generator from one terminal, through the circuit, and back to the generator by the other terminal. No current is ever lost, the amount of current which returns to the generator being exactly equal to the amount of current which flows out of it. A circuit will be a d.c. circuit if the supply or generator is a d.c. supply such as either a battery, a dynamo or a power-supply unit (PSU) which converts the alternating-current mains supply into d.c.

In an a.c. circuit, current again flows in all parts of the circuit, but current flow is *in each direction alternately*. One complete cycle of alternating current starts with current flowing in one direction, increasing in value to a maximum or peak, then decreasing, reducing to zero, and finally reversing its direction of flow. This current flowing in the reverse direction in turn builds up to a peak and falls again to zero, before reversing to start the cycle all over again.

The number of complete cycles of such alternating current flow which take place in one second is called the *frequency* of the a.c. It is measured in hertz (Hz), one Hz being one complete cycle of current per second.

Two common circuit faults are open circuit (o/c) and short circuit (s/c) (see Figure 5.2). An open-circuit fault is one in which the circuit is broken in such a way that current can no longer flow through it. A short-circuit fault is one in which an unwanted connection is made such that current flow takes the wrong path or paths. Such o/c or s/c faults in electronic circuits are generally caused by failure of individual components in the circuit.

Exercise 5.1
Construct the simple circuit shown in Figure 5.3. The supply can be either a mains PSU or a 6V accumulator. Every switch controls a light bulb which is in series with the switch, but the switch-controlled circuits are all in parallel with one another.

How many bulbs can be switched on, one after the other, in this circuit before the fuse blows and interrupts the circuit?

The effects of current flow in an electrical circuit

Current flowing in a circuit gives rise to the following effects:

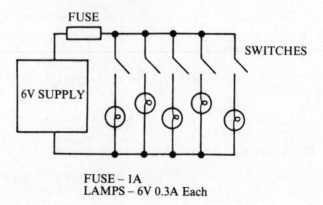

FUSE – 1A
LAMPS – 6V 0.3A Each

Figure 5.3   A simple circuit

(a) A heating effect. Any conductor which carries a current will become hot because of the movement of electrons through the conductor's resistance (see Chapter 12)
(b) A magnetic effect. Any wire carrying a current will start to behave like a magnet (see Chapter 11)
(c) A chemical effect. A current passed through a solution of a salty material dissolved in water will cause a chemical change in the solution which can release corrosive substances.

Both d.c. and a.c. give rise to identical *heating* effects. The *magnetic* effect of alternating current is to produce magnetism which changes direction every time the current through the wire changes direction. The *chemical* effect of a.c. is negligible, because appreciable chemical action takes place only after current has been flowing in one direction for some time.

All of these effects are put to practical use – the heating effect in electric fires and ovens, for instance, the magnetic effect in electric motors, relays and solenoids, and the chemical effect in battery charging and electroplating. At the same time, all these effects of current flow can produce undesirable results. Examples are the overheating of circuit components, unwanted interference from the magnetic fields created around wires, and corrosion caused by the chemical action on damp materials.

Electrical circuits can contain more than one load, and any of these loads can be connected either in series, in parallel, or in series-parallel – all as illustrated in Figure 5.4. These types of connection have been described in Chapter 4 but not their fault-finding aspects.

When several loads are connected in series, the failure of any one load in such a way that it becomes open-circuit (o/c) is enough to prevent any current flowing in the circuit. If one load fails short-circuit (s/c), however, total circuit resistance will be reduced and more current will flow.

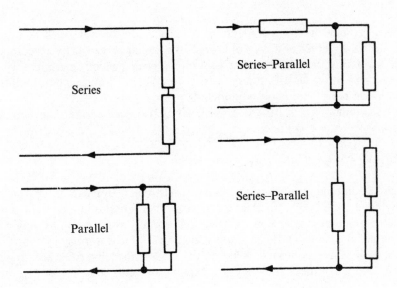

Figure 5.4   Loads in series, in parallel and in series-parallel

When loads are connected in parallel, the o/c failure of one load will not affect current flow through any other load, though the total current drawn from the supply will be less. If one load fails s/c, however, all other loads will be by-passed and no current will flow through them. Current flow through the short-circuit will however, be large, and can often cause damage unless a fuse blows or a contact-breaker opens.

Both types of failure will have simultaneous effects on the series-parallel circuit. Failure of the series load(s) will cause zero current to flow in the whole circuit if the failure is o/c, increased current if the failure is s/c. An o/c failure of a parallel load will cause a decrease in total current flow, though the current through the remaining parallel leads will generally increase. An s/c failure of a parallel load will deprive all other parallel load(s) of current, but the total amount of current flowing in the circuit will still be limited by the load connected in series.

Electronic circuits generally operate with smaller values of current flow than do 'heavy' electrical circuits. Moreover, both a.c. and d.c. often flow together in electronic circuits; and both the frequencies and the waveforms of the a.c. are very different from those which are derived from the mains electrical supply. Nevertheless, all the basic principles of supply, fusing, switches, the use of conductors and the dissipation of heat in a load apply as fully to an electronic circuit as they do to any other electrical circuit.

Electronic components

All electronic circuits are made up of a selection of electronic components connected together in a way indicated in a *circuit diagram*. Every component plays a part in the circuit, and it is the circuit design which determines what the circuit as a whole will do. A large variety of different circuits can be built from a small number of electronic components.

These components can be classified into two categories. They are either *passive* or *active* components.

Passive components

Passive components include all those whose circuit action can be measured by a single quantity – e.g. resistance in a resistor, capacitance in a capacitor, inductance in an inductor or coil. No electronic circuit which contains only passive components can generate or amplify the power of waveforms. By contrast, the action of active components needs to be described by reference to several measured quantities; and they are capable of generating waveforms and of power amplification.

Resistors are used in a circuit either to control the amount of current flowing in the circuit, or to control voltage by means of the *potential divider* circuit. Fixed resistors, as their name suggests, have fixed values of resistance, and are obtainable in preferred values (see Chapter 4). *Variable* resistors, or *potentiometers*, can be adjusted by hand. A *preset* or *trimmer* potentiometer is one whose value is set, usually by a screwdriver adjustment, when the circuit is first tested and is not altered (save to correct a fault condition) after that time.

The symbols which are used in circuit diagrams to designate resistors are shown in Figure 5.5. When a variable resistor is indicated, two of the three terminals of a potentiometer are used, the central (slider) terminal and one only of the two others.

Figure 5.6. shows the working principle of the potentiometer, which is in effect a variable potential divider. A sector of a circle, or of a straight strip, of resistive material is connected at each end to fixed terminals, and a sliding contact is held against the resistive material by a spring leaf. As the position of the sliding contact is altered, so will different values of resistance be created between the sliding contact and each of the two fixed terminals.

A variety of potentiometer circuit using a switch with separate fixed resistors is the *switched potentiometer*, the principle of which is shown in Figure 5.7. The switch contact can be moved to connect to any of the points where resistors join, so that a number of potential divider circuits can be formed. There will clearly be a different value of voltage division at each contact point.

All resistors, whether fixed or variable, are specified by reference to their resistance value, their method of construction and their power rating. The

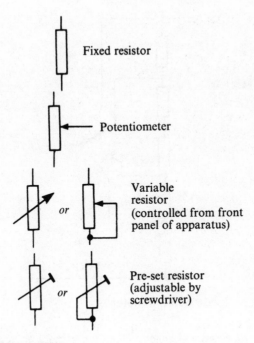

Fixed resistor

Potentiometer

Variable
resistor
(controlled from front
panel of apparatus)

Pre-set resistor
(adjustable by
screwdriver)

Figure 5.5   Resistor symbols

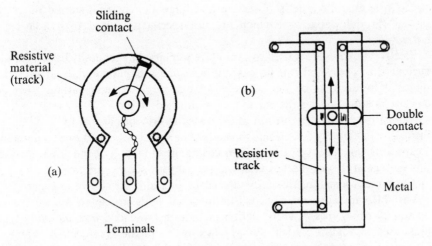

Sliding
contact

Resistive
material
(track)

Terminals

(a)

(b)

Double
contact

Resistive
track

Metal

Figure 5.6   Potentiometer consuction: (a) circular; (b) slide

abbreviation 'ww' is commonly used to denote *wire-wound* resistors.

Several different types of construction are used to make both *fixed* and *variable capacitors*. Small fixed capacitors use mica or a ceramic as their

73

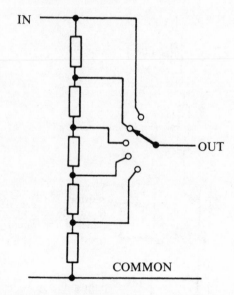

Figure 5.7 A switched potentiometer

insulation (or *dielectric*). Larger values use paper, polyester, polystyrene or polycarbonate plastics; while capacitors of the largest values of capacitance are of electrolytic construction. The voltage rating, particularly with electrolytic capacitors, must be strictly observed, and large a.c. currents should never be passed through capacitors which are not specifically rated to handle such currents.

Electrolytic capacitors used to smooth power supplies generally have a 'ripple current rating' printed on the case. When such a capacitor fails, it must be replaced by another of the same or greater ripple current rating. ('Ripple current' is a fluctuating a.c. current superimposed on d.c.).

Capacitors, since they do not allow a steady flow of current to pass, act as insulators in a purely d.c. circuit. A sudden change of voltage at one terminal of a capacitor will, however, cause an equal change of voltage at the other, though this voltage at the second terminal will persist for only a short time.

The symbols used for capacitors in circuit diagrams are shown in Figure 5.8.

Variable capacitors are used with only small values of capacitance, ranging up to 500 pF. Types of construction include the so-called *meshing-plate* type illustrated in Figure 5.9, the *beehive* trimmer, and the *compression* trimmer. Capacitor values are measured in pF (picofarads) for the smallest sizes, in nF (nanofarads) for intermediate sizes, and in μF (microfarads) for the largest sizes. (Note that 1000 pF = 1nF and 1000 nF = 1 μF; so that 0.1 μF = 100 nF, 0.1 nF = 100 pF, and so on.)

When a colour code is used to indicate capacitance values, the units are given

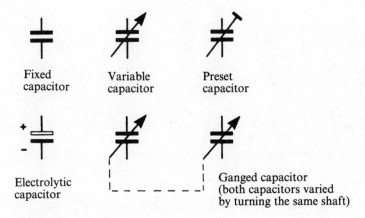

Figure 5.8 Capacitor symbols

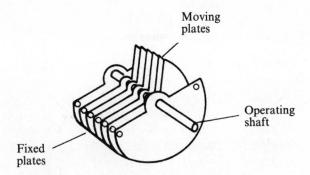

Figure 5.9 A meshing-plate type of variable capacitor

in pF. For example, a coding of brown, black, yellow indicates 100 000 pF (which is also, of course, either 100 nF or 0.1 μF).

When an alternating voltage is applied to a capacitor, an alternating current will flow and the ratio V/I (V across the capacitor, I through the capacitor) is called the *capacitive reactance*, units ohms. Unlike resistance, capacitive reactance is *not* a constant for a capacitor but varies according to the frequency of the alternating voltage. The higher the frequency, the lower is the capacitive reactance for a given capacitor. In an equation, this is:

$$X_c = \frac{1}{2\pi fC}$$

where f = frequency in Hz, C = capacitance in Farads.

Inductors and transformers, the circuit symbols for which are shown in Figure 5.10, are less used than the other components save in radio-frequency

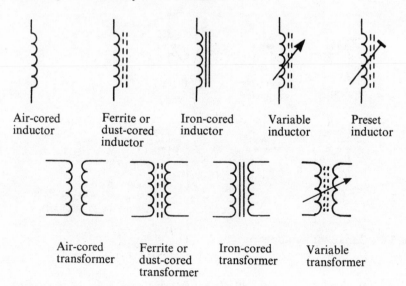

Air-cored inductor Ferrite or dust-cored inductor Iron-cored inductor Variable inductor Preset inductor

Air-cored transformer Ferrite or dust-cored transformer Iron-cored transformer Variable transformer

Figure 5.10 Inductor and transformer symbols

amplifiers and oscillators. An *inductor* consists of a coil of wire – which may be either unsupported, wound on a hollow former, or wound on a former fitted with a core of metal or other magnetic material.

Air-cored inductors – either a self-supporting coil or a coil wound on a hollow plastic former – are used for the higher radio frequencies above about 100 MHz; ferrite or iron-dust cores for frequencies between about 100 kHz and 100 MHz; and cores of laminated steel (thin strips of metal) for frequencies below 100 kHz. Inductors intended to handle signals at low frequencies need to be large, heavy objects.

All inductors pass d.c. current freely, since the wire used for their windings has a low resistance; but they offer much more opposition to the flow of a.c. In this respect, inductors act in the opposite way to capacitors.

The combination of an inductor and a capacitor connected in parallel (Figure 5.11) provides very high resistance to a.c. current flowing at a particular frequency, called the *resonant frequency*.

When an alternating voltage is applied to an inductor, an alternating current will flow and the ratio V/I (V across the inductor, I through the inductor) is called the *inductive reactance*, units ohms. Unlike resistance, inductive reactance is *not* a constant for an inductor but varies according to the frequency of the alternating voltage. The higher the frequency, the higher is the inductive reactance for a given inductor. In an equation, this is:

$$X_c = 2\pi fL$$

where f = frequency in Hz, L = inductance in Henries.

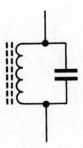

Figure 5.11   A parallel-resonant circuit

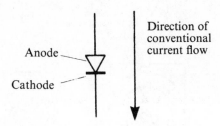

Figure 5.12   Diode symbol

Transformers are constructed like inductors, but with more than one winding on their core. One winding is supplied with an a.c. signal and is called the *primary winding*. The other windings are called *secondary windings*. An a.c. signal voltage will be induced across the ends of each secondary winding whenever an a.c. signal is connected to the primary winding, even though the winding wires are not physically joined. There is no output from a secondary winding when only direct current flows steadily through the primary winding. The action of inductors and transformers is covered in more detail in Chapter 11.

The *diode* is a component which allows current to flow through it in one direction only. It has two terminals, called its anode and cathode respectively. See Figure 5.12. It conducts current when its anode is positive and its cathode negative in a circuit. When its anode is at a negative voltage compared to its cathode, a diode behaves like a very high resistance.

When a diode conducts, its resistance is not constant but varies according to the amount of current flowing. A diode therefore does *not* obey Ohm's Law.

The cathode connection of a diode is usually marked with a white dot or band. In large stud-mounted diodes, the stud is generally used as the cathode connection; but it is still safer to check with the maker's information sheet, or to test as follows.

To find the cathode connection of an unmarked diode, use the simple circuit

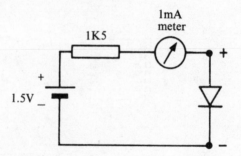

Figure 5.13   Finding the polarity of a diode

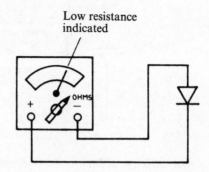

Figure 5.14   A multimeter used to find diode polarity

of Figure 5.13. When the meter indicates that a current is flowing, it means that the *negative* lead must be connected to the *cathode*.

A multimeter can also be used to check diode polarity (see Figure 5.14), using its lowest resistance range. Because of the internal connections of the meter, the diode conducts when the red (+) lead of the meter is in contact with the cathode and the black (−) lead in contact with the anode. When a multimeter is switched to a resistance-measuring range, the battery negative is normally connected to the red (+) lead.

It is important to remember that a good diode will have a low resistance to current flow in one direction, the so-called forward direction, but a very high resistance to current flow in the opposite or *reverse biased direction*.

Active components

The active components most frequently met are transistors, thyristors, integrated circuits (ICs) and cathode-ray tubes (see Chapter 14).

Transistors have three main connections, named respectively *emitter, base* and *collector*. A fourth connection is sometimes made to the casing. Before a

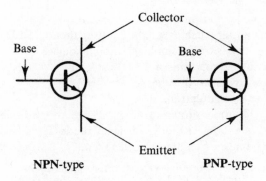

Figure 5.15   Transistor symbols

transistor can be connected into a circuit, the layout of these three connections must be identified from the manufacturer's data sheets.

The symbols used for the two basic types of transistor are shown in Figure 5.15. *The arrowed lead is always the emitter,* and the direction of the arrow shows the direction of current flow (*conventionally taken as positive-to-negative*) through the base and emitter terminals. When the arrowhead points *towards the base*, the symbol represents a *PNP transistor*. When the arrowhead points *away from the base*, the symbol represents a *NPN transistor*.

The table below sets out the European transistor numbering system, as standardized by the Pro-Electron Organization, whose headquarters are in Brussels.

THE PRO-ELECTRON NUMBERING SYSTEM FOR TRANSISTORS
The first letter of the code number indicates the type of semiconductor material used in the transistor:
A ... Germanium
B ... Silicon
C ... Gallium arsenide, or similar
D ... Indium antimonide, or similar
E ... Photoconductive materials

The second letter indicates the type of construction or the main use of the transistor or other semiconductor device:
A ... Detector diode: high-speed diode: mixer diode
B ... Variable-capacitance (varicap) diode
C ... Transistor used for audio-frequency, not for power, amplification
D ... Power transistor usable at audio frequencies
E ... Tunnel diode
F ... Transistor for radio-frequency amplifiers (low-power)
G ... Multiple transistors on the same (probably silicon) chip
L ... Power transistor usable at radio frequencies

P ... Light or other radiation detector
Q ... Radiation emitter (such as a light-emitting diode – LED)
R ... Low-power thyristor (or similar) switching device
S ... Low-power switching transistor
T ... High-power thyristor, or other, controller
U ... High-power switching transistor
X ... Frequency-multiplier diode: varactor: step-recovery diode
Y ... Rectifier diode: booster diode: efficiency diode
Z ... Voltage-reference or regulator (Zener) diode

Figures or letters following the second letter indicate the design type of the component. A three-figure serial number indicates a 'consumer-type' component such as would be used in domestic radio, TV, tape recorders, audio, etc. A letter W, X, Y or Z followed by two figures denotes a device for professional or military use in such roles as transmission, telecommunications, computing, etc.

The United States numbering system consists only of the number/letter combination 2N, followed by a serial number. This serial number gives no information except about the age of the design – high numbers indicating the more recent designs. To get full data on US transistor types (or on Japanese transistor types which use a '2S' coding), the manufacturer must be identified and his data sheets consulted. Collected data books for most American, Japanese and European transistor types can, however, be obtained.

Transistors are connected into circuit by soldering the wire leads of the transistor on to a circuit board. Some types (namely, power transistors) have only two separate leads, using the metal case of the transistor as the collector. (See Figure 5.16.) Such transistors are bolted into place, the collector connection being then made to a solder-tag held down by one of the fixing-bolts. Small transistors are light enough to be supported only with lead-out wires soldered to circuit board.

Thyristors also have three connections, known as *anode, cathode* and *gate* respectively. Small thyristors used in such applications as light dimmers look like small transistors. Large thyristors used for the control of motor speeds, etc. are shaped like power transistors or stud-mounted diodes with one connection made to the metal stud.

Figure 5.17 shows that the word 'large' is used above in a comparative sense only. Most thyristors are quite small objects in absolute terms.

Integrated circuits (ICs) have no special symbol, because their range and variety is too great to make a symbol system possible. The IC consists of a complete miniature circuit of transistors and resistors (sometimes of low-value capacitors also), constructed of silicon and designed to perform a complete circuit function. Some ICs have transistor-like cases, with up to seven lead-out wires.

More common is the *'dual-in-line'* (DIL) pattern with two rows of pins.

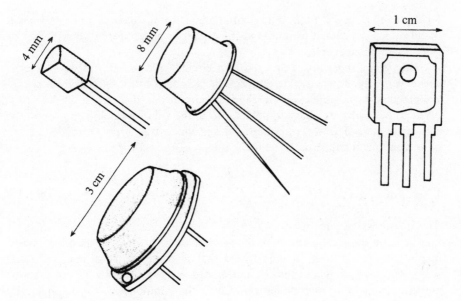

Figure 5.16   Transistor cases

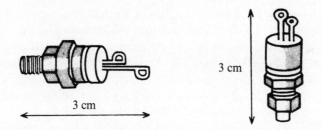

Figure 5.17   Cases for large thyristors

Standard DIL cases exist for 8-pin, 14-pin, 16-pin and other numbers up to 40-pin ICs. Spacing between the pins in a line is standardized at 2.5 mm (0.1″). The spacing between lines is set at 7.5 mm (0.3″) for small ICs and at 15 mm (0.6″) for larger types.

ICs are connected into circuit either by direct soldering or by means of holders. When holders are used, they are soldered to a printed circuit board (PCB) so that the circuit can be completed and checked before the ICs themselves are inserted.

It will often be necessary in service work to check the values of either d.c. or a.c. voltages at every lead-out of a transistor or at every pin of an IC. To avoid having to remove the PCB, many commercial circuits have test points – small metal pillars connected to points in the circuit at which important voltages or signals can be measured.

Cathode ray tubes are connected into circuits in a variety of ways. A base socket is nearly always used to connect the pins on the tube base, and the socket is connected by flexible cables to the main circuit board. In addition, however, other connections may have to be made with the aid of wire clips to pins on the side of the tube. The necessary high-voltage connection is always made to a pin or sunken metal cup situated near the screen of the cathode ray tube.

Constructing circuits

The methods that are used industrially to construct circuit boards in large numbers are quite different from the methods that have to be used for experimental or one-off circuits. One factor that is common to all constructional methods, however, is that the circuit diagram is a way of showing connections which does not give any indication of how the components can be physically arranged on a board.

The main difference between circuit diagrams and layout diagrams is that on a layout diagram any crossing of connecting leads has to be avoided. A component such as a resistor or capacitor can cross a circuit-connecting track because on a conventional printed circuit board (PCB) the component will be on the opposite side of the board from the track (but see Surface mounting, later in this chapter). The simplest circuits to lay out are discrete transistor amplifiers; the most difficult are digital circuits in which each chip contains a large number of separate devices.

Small-scale circuits can be laid out manually, using cardboard cut-outs of the components, with connections and internal circuits marked, on a large sheet of tracing paper or on transparent plastic which has been marked with a pattern of dots at 0.1″ centres. The designing is done looking at the component side of the board, and will start by roughing out a practicable layout which does not require any track cross-overs. At this stage, it is important to show any interconnecting points, using edge connections or fixed sockets, because it must be possible to take leads to these connectors without cross-overs. This can be quite difficult when the connection pattern is fixed in advance, as for example when a standard form of connection like a stereo DIN socket or a Centronics printer socket is to be used.

This layout can then be improved, with particular attention paid to durability and servicing. The positions of presets and other adjustments will have to be arranged, along with points where test voltages can be measured, so that servicing and adjustment will be comparatively easy. Signal lines may have to be re-routed to avoid having lines running parallel for more than a few millimetres (because of stray capacitances), or to keep high-impedance connections away from power supply leads. Some tracks that carry RF may need to be screened, so that earthed tracks must be provided to which metal screens can be soldered. Components which will run hot, such as high-wattage resistors, will have to be mounted clear of other components so that they do not cause breakdown because of overheating in semiconductors or capacitors. One way of achieving this is to use long leads for these components so that they stand well clear of the board, but this is not always a feasible solution if several boards have to be mounted near to each other.

More extensive circuits can be planned by computer, so that the PCB pattern is printed out after details of each component and each join in the circuit have been typed into the computer. Even computer-produced layouts, however, may have to be manually adjusted to avoid having unwanted stray capacitances appearing between components. Either method will have to take account of the physical differences that can exist between similar components, such as length of tubular capacitors and the difference between axial and radial lead positions.

One-off and experimental circuits can be constructed on matrix boards (also known as stripboards), and the layout that is used on these boards can be used also as a pattern for manufacturing PCBs for mass production. In either case, a board material must be used which will be strong and heat-resistant, with good electrical insulation. The choice will usually be between plastic-impregnated glass fibre board, or SRBP (synthetic resin-bonded paper), though some special-purpose circuits may have to be laid out on ceramic (like porcelain) or vitreous (like glass) materials in order to cope with high temperature use and flame-proofing requirements.

Whatever type of board is used will be covered with copper to act as the connections between components. On a matrix board, the copper will be laid out in strips, usually 0.1" apart and drilled with holes for lead-out wires also at 0.1" centres, see Figure 5.19. Boards for larger-scale production are undrilled and completely covered with copper, which will then be etched away into the pattern of connections that is needed. For mass production, the processes are completely automated, and the assembly of the components on to the board and subsequent soldering will also be totally automatic, see Figure 5.18.

Many commercial PCBs, particularly for computer or other digital applications, are double-sided, with tracks on the component side as well as on the conventional track side. Where connections are needed between sides, plated-through holes are used. These are holes which have copper on each side and which have been electroplated with copper so that the holes have become partly-filled, making a copper contact between the sides. These connections are strengthened when the board is soldered.

The use of double-sided board is particularly important for digital circuits where a single-sided board presents difficulties because of the need to cross leads. The use of a well-designed double-sided board can solve these problems, but

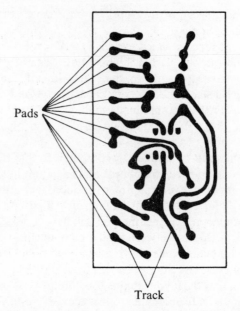

Pads

Track

Figure 5.18   A typical PC board, showing tracks and soldering pads

care needs to be taken over capacitances between tracks that are on opposite sides of the board.

Surface mounting

Surface-mounting technology (SMT) has been in use for some time, certainly since 1977, but only recently has its use become widespread. Components for surface mounting use flat tabs in place of wire leads, and because these tabs can be short the inductance of the leads is greatly reduced. The tabs are soldered directly to pads formed on to the board, so that there are always tracks on the component side of the board. Most SMT boards are two-sided, so that tracks also exist on the other side of the board.

The use of SMT results in manufacturers being able to offer components that are physically smaller, but with connections that dissipate heat more readily, are mechanically stronger and have lower electrical resistance and lower self-inductance. Some components can be made so small that it is impossible to mark a value or a code number on to them. This presents no problems for automated assembly, since the packet need only be inserted into the correct hopper in the assembly machine, but considerable care needs to be taken when replacing such components, which should be kept in their packing until they are soldered into place. Machine assembly of SMT components is followed by automatic soldering processes, which nowadays usually involve the use of solder-paint (which

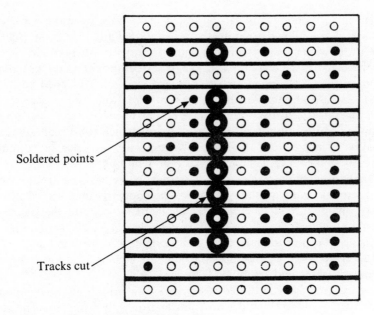

Figure 5.19   A matrix strip-board circuit

also retains components in place until they are soldered) and heating by blowing hot nitrogen gas over the board. Solder-baths are still used, but the hot-gas method causes less mechanical disturbance and can also allow heat-sensitive components to be shielded.

Considerable care is needed for hand-soldering and unsoldering SMT components. A pair of tweezers can be used to grip the component, but it is better to use a holding-arm with a miniature clamp, so that both hands can be free. The problem is that the soldering pads and the component itself can be so small that it is difficult to ensure that a component is in the correct place. Desoldering presents equal difficulties – it is difficult to ensure that the correct component is being desoldered, and almost impossible to identify the component after removal. A defective SMT component should be put into a 'rejects' bin immediately after removal.

Small-scale circuit production

The simplest form of construction for a one-off circuit is the matrix stripboard. This can be obtained in a wide range of sizes, up to 119 × 455 mm (4.7″ × 18″ approx.). Tracks can be cut by a 'spot-cutter' tool which can be used in a hand or electric drill, this allowing components like DIL ICs to be mounted without shorting the pin connections, see Figure 5.19. Once these cuts have been made, the components can be soldered on to the board and the circuit tested.

Arrangement of components can be tested in advance by using a *solderless breadboard*, which allows components to be inserted and held by spring clips, using a layout which is essentially the same as for matrix stripboards.

The alternative is the one-off PCB. The pattern of the circuit tracks has to be drawn on a piece of copper-laminated board, using a felt-tipped pen which contains etch-resistant ink. An alternative is to work from a transparency of the pattern, using light-sensitive etch-resistive material which is then 'developed' in a sodium hydroxide solution. When the ink or other etch-resist is dry, the board is etched in a ferric chloride bath (acid hazard – wear goggles, gloves and an apron) until all the unwanted copper has been removed.

In a mass-production process, the pattern of etch-resist is placed on to the copper by a silk-screen printing process. The copper is then etched in baths which are maintained at a constant high temperature, and the boards are washed thoroughly in water, followed by demineralized (soft) water, and then finally in alcohol so as to make drying more rapid. For the hand-made etched board, all traces of the resist material and the etching solution have to be removed by washing and scrubbing with wire wool.

The board can then be drilled, using a 1 mm drill, and the components inserted. The final action is soldering, using an iron with a small tip. The boards are heat-resistant, not heat-proof, so that soldering should be done fairly quickly, never keeping the iron in contact with the copper for too long. Excessive heating will loosen the copper from the plastic board, or burn the board, and if the copper has been cleaned correctly and all components leads are equally clean, soldering should be very rapid. Chemical tinning solutions can be used to treat the copper of the board so that soldering can be even more rapid. Remember that excessive heat will not only damage the board but also the more susceptible components like semiconductors and capacitors. The time needed to obtain a good soldered joint should not exceed a few seconds.

Laying out a printed circuit

A circuit can be laid out on matrix board by following a simple set of rules. First, the *circuit junctions* must be found. A circuit junction is a place where components are connected either to one another or to wires leading from or to the PCB. On a matrix or PCB every circuit junction is represented by a separate strip or area of copper. Figure 5.20 shows some examples of circuit junctions (*ringed*), such as would be found in simple circuits.

Once identified and ringed with a pencil on the circuit diagram, the circuit junctions are *numbered*, starting with 1 for the junction which takes in the (+) supply line. When the circuit contains a transistor, it is an advantage to have the circuit junctions for the three transistor connections numbered consecutively – i.e. 3, 4, 5 or 8, 9, 10 – so that transistors with short lead-out wires can be used.

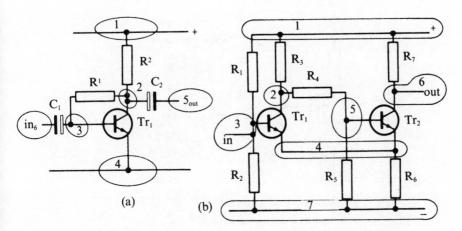

Figure 5.20   Marking and numbering cuircuit junctions on a diagram

When the junctions have been numbered, the circuit can be built on to matrix boards with numbered strips. Some types of matrix board are numbered during manufacture. Others can be numbered by gumming paper strips on to each side at the ends of the tracks and numbering the tracks on the paper.

An alternative is to coat each side of the board at the ends with one of the white fluid materials which are used for correcting typing errors (sold under such names as *Snopaque* and *Tipp-Ex*). These fluids dry very rapidly, leaving a matte white surface on which it is easy to write.

Once the numbering is complete, the components are soldered in place to the tracks whose numbers are shown in the circuit diagram, prepared as already described. To take the example of Figure 5.20(a) . R_1 is soldered between Tracks 2 and 3, R_2 between Tracks 1 and 2, C_1 between Tracks 6 and 3 with the positive end on Track 3, and C_2 between Tracks 2 and 5 with the positive end on Track 2. The transistor is connected with its emitter to Track 4, its base to Track 3, and its collector to Track 2. The supply is taken to Tracks 1 (+) and 4 (−), the input signal to Track 6 and the output signal from Track 5.

Figure 5.21 shows a variation of this method which is particularly suitable for symmetrical circuits such as the multivibrator circuit illustrated. A central track is used for the negative supply line, and two separate tracks linked by a wire soldered to each are used for the positive line.

The layout of a circuit on to copper laminate board should start by making a drawing on tracing paper or transparent film. Components, or cardboard cut-outs can then be placed on the drawing to show sizes, and to mark in the mounting pads to which the leads will be soldered. This is been done with the drawing representing the component side of the board, but the tracks can now be drawn in as they will exist on the copper side – this means that the actual appearance of the component side will be the mirror-image of your layout.

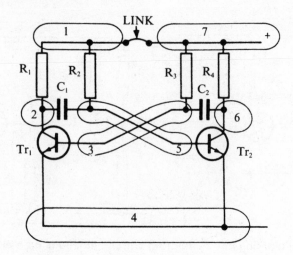

Figure 5.21   Another type of numbering system

The drawing will then have to be transferred to the copper. This can be done manually, using an etch-resistant ink as described earlier, or by photographic methods. The board can then be etched, thoroughly cleaned, drilled and then the components mounted and soldered into place.

Soldering and desoldering

Soldering is a way of joining metals by melting a metal alloy of lead and tin on to the other metals. Metals that are to be joined in this way must be compatible (aluminium needs special treatment), thoroughly clean, and should be mechanically joined so that the soldered joint is not expected to provide support as well as electrical connection unless the amount of support is minor. The main obstacle to good soldering is dirt, and thorough cleaning is the most important part of good soldering, whether by hand or by automatic solder-bath methods.

Soldering irons (despite the name, the business end is made from copper) are available in various sizes, and for electronics use, a 15W type along with a 25W type will cover most of the circuit requirements, though a larger iron is useful for some specialized tasks. For some heavier work, a fast-heating low-voltage iron can be useful, and for some types of servicing a battery-operated 6W iron may be needed. Some irons can have desoldering attachments clipped on, and a set of these will be needed unless other desoldering methods are used. The desoldering provision should be a solder-pump, described later in this chapter.

The tips of bits should be kept clean and in their correct shapes. The copper bits can dissolve quite rapidly in some types of solder, though many solder formulations contain some copper to inhibit this action. A supply of spare bits,

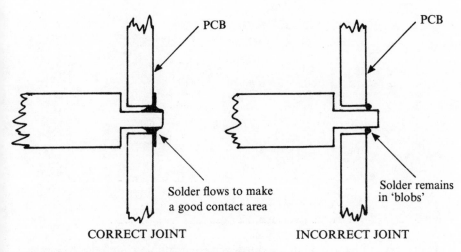

Solder flows to make
a good contact area

Solder remains
in 'blobs'

CORRECT JOINT   INCORRECT JOINT

Figure 5.22   Correct and incorrect soldering

and a spare element for each type of iron, should be stocked. Scale should be removed from the main body of the iron at intervals, and the earth resistance checked, because an earthed iron is safer to use, particularly for modern types of ICs.

Solder should be of the flux-cored variety, but a tin of flux should be kept handy in case of large soldering jobs. Having a separate tin of flux also makes it much easier to 'tin' (coat with solder) large surfaces of metal using non-cored solder and either a large iron or a miniature blowlamp.

To solder a joint effectively, the metals should first be thoroughly cleaned, and in some cases it is preferable to tin both. They should then be mechanically connected by twisting wire, bending tags etc. so that the metals will not depend on the solder for mechanical strength. The iron is allowed to heat thoroughly until it will instantly melt a piece of flux-cored solder held to the tip. The tip should be kept clean just before use by wiping it with a slightly damp cloth – never flick excess solder from the tip of an iron.

The iron is held against the metals that are to be joined for a few seconds so as to heat them, and then the solder is applied to where the tip of the iron contacts the joint. The solder will melt and spread over the joint, and as soon as the solder makes a smooth joint, the iron can be removed. Never hold the iron in place longer than is needed to allow the solder to become smooth like this, as excessive heat will burn off the flux, allow the solder to oxidize in the air, and ruin the electrical and mechanical soundness of the joint. Figure 5.22 shows the different between correct and incorrect solder flow.

A few types of metals are notoriously difficult to solder, including spring steel and some of the nickel alloys that are used for heating elements. These need scrupulous cleaning, often with acid washes, and should be tinned beforehand.

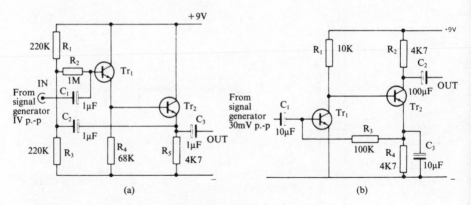

Figure 5.23   Circuits for Exercise 5.2

Large pieces of metal should be tinned using a small blowlamp. Heat-sensitive components require rather different treatment. The leads of transistors should be gripped by pliers so as to act as a heat-shunt, preventing the heat of the iron from reaching the casing of the transistor. ICs cannot be gripped in this way, but it is usually possible to clamp a 'bulldog' type of clip over the roots of the pins. Particular care should be taken to avoid excessive heating on any electronic components, but semiconductors and some capacitors are by far the most susceptible to damage.

Desoldering should preferably be done with a 'solder-pump' or sucker. This is a spring-loaded suction pump with a PTFE nozzle. The plunger is depressed, expelling the air and the nozzle held to the joint which is to be desoldered. A hot soldering iron is applied and when the solder is fluid, the plunger is released by pressing the trigger button. This action sucks the molten solder into the pump body, from where it can be removed at intervals.

Exercise 5.2
Identify the circuit junctions in the circuits shown in Figure 5.23(a) and (b). Draw them in, and check them carefully. Build the circuits either on matrix board or by plugging the component wires into '*solderless breadboards*', and apply the voltages shown. (TR$_1$ and TR$_2$ are general purpose NPN transistors.)

The circuits, when operating correctly, will each give an output waveform which will appear on the screen of an oscilloscope as shown in Figure 5.24

Some notes on boxes and panels

Boxes and panels can often be bought ready-made, but they may sometimes have to be made up for a particular circuit. Thin strips of steel or aluminium are cut out with snips, and flattened in a vice. The lines along which metal needs to

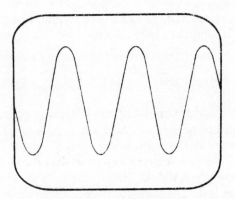

Figure 5.24   Shape of correct output waveform from circuits of Figure 5.2

be bent are marked out, the bending being done with the aid of a vice and a pair of metal plates. Edges can be brazed, soldered, welded or simply lapped over and secured by self-tapping screws or pop-rivets.

Panels are best drilled with a bench-drill. Large holes can be cut with hole-punches of the *Osmor* or *Q-max* types. All holes, of whatever size, should be de-burred with a file to clean off ragged edges. Holes drilled to take cables need to be particularly carefully de-burred, and rubber grommets should then be fitted to prevent the cable being chafed. A cable clamp prevents strain on the attachment of the wires of the cable to the main switch. Plastic boxes are also used extensively for small-scale circuits. These make drilling and cutting much easier.

Circuit boards should be fixed firmly inside the box, but need to be connected in such a way that both sides of the board can be reached for servicing operations. It is particularly necessary that leads to such panel components as potentiometers and switches should be made through cables long enough to permit the circuit board to be lifted out from the box in case the components in question need to be checked or replaced.

Fault tracing techniques

Basic fault finding in both analogue and digital systems follows similar principles. A source is required to inject suitable signals into the input and the signal processing is then monitored as it passes through the system on a stage-by-stage basis. For analogue systems a suitable input source is a signal generator, while an oscilloscope can be used as a monitor. For digital systems this end-to-end technique can be carried out using a logic pulser to provide the inputs while the processing can be monitored with a logic probe. A technique that is often used with speed advantage is known as the *half split* method. Here the system is divided into two sections and the end-to-end technique used to find the faulty half. This process is repeated continually until the faulty stage is identified.

Tools and their correct use

Electronics servicing and minor constructional work requires a small number of tools, but these need to be used correctly and kept in good condition. Correct use of tools is as important from the safety point of view as it is for carrying out the work correctly. You are required as part of the practical test for the C & G 224 course to identify a standard list of tools and state which tools will be required for a given task. The standard list is:

Screwdrivers
Drills and drilling machines
Files
Wire cutters
Pliers
Wire strippers
Soldering iron
Desoldering tools
Hacksaws
Crimping tools
Marking out tools

– and you will be asked to describe how these tools should be maintained in good condition.

A set of screwdrivers will be needed, ranging in size from the watchmaker's type (1 mm blade) up to a large-bladed type for unfastening panels from rack assemblies. Insulated handles are essential – all-metal screwdrivers should never be used for electronics work because of the risk of shorting, since the smaller screwdrivers will be used extensively for adjusting trimmers with voltages applied to the circuit. The blades may be sharpened carefully to keep the original shape indicated in Figure 5.25. Note that cross-point screwdrivers cannot be reground or sharpened.

Screwdrivers must never be used to prise open cases or as cutting tools. Blades can be damaged if a screw is rusted or otherwise jammed in place, so that if reasonable force does not undo a screw, it should be loosened by using one of the many patent lubricants, such as WD-40. Sometimes a seized-up screw can be loosed by a hammer-blow applied to the screw-head with an old screwdriver, but this may cause damage to electronics equipment. By far the better method is to drill out a seized-up screw so that it can be replaced.

Drilling can be done with a hand-drill, a portable electric drill or a bench-

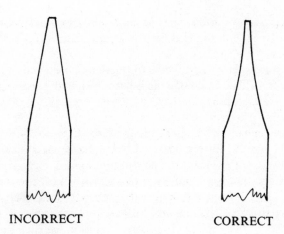

INCORRECT   CORRECT

Figure 5.25   Cross section of screwdriver

drill. For much servicing work, a battery-operated portable electric drill can be very useful. The work to be drilled must be securely clamped – never try to hold the drill in one hand and the work in the other. Some electronics boards can be very difficult to clamp adequately, and a better solution is to lay the board on a flat sheet of a material such as Blu-tack. Drills should be matched to the work, and for most electronics purposes a set of carbon-steel drill-bits will be suitable. Drills for cutting steel need to be harder, and high-speed drill-bits are more appropriate for such hard metals.

When the drill allows a choice of speeds, use the speed that is appropriate for the type of drill-bit and its size. The larger drill-bits should be used at a slower speed than the smaller ones, and the maker's instructions observed for special-ized bit types. Brush away all of the swarf after drilling, and clean up drilled holes with a countersink, a small file, or a wire brush. Sometimes hand use of a larger size bit can be an effective way of cleaning up a drilled hole. Observe safety precautions while using any drill, tying back loose clothing (a tie is particularly dangerous) and using goggles to protect the eyes. Keep both hands well away from the work that is being drilled.

Drill-bits become blunt after use, and should be inspected and re-sharpened regularly. Re-sharpening is a skilled job which can be made much easier by using one of the jigs or re-sharpening tools that can be bought in toolshops. Very great care should be taken to avoid altering the cutting angle of a bit because this can make it quite useless.

Files will be needed in a range of sizes. The larger sizes are unlikely to be used much, but a good selection of miniature files, called Swiss files or watchmaker's files, will be needed, and a few medium-cut and final-cut files in 6″ and 9″ lengths will be useful. The miniature files will come in for heavier use in servicing work, and need to be maintained well. In particular, a file needs to be cleaned well after being used on softer types of materials, particularly aluminium or its alloys. A wire brush can be used for the larger files, but is less useful for the miniature types.

Never use files as sharp instruments for piercing holes, and never use them as scribers or as levers. The metal of a file is hardened, and a bending force is likely to shatter the metal, a potential hazard to your eyes. When a file becomes too blunt for effective use, replace it because it cannot be restored.

Wire-cutters, strippers and pliers are often used together, with the pliers used to hold a cable and the cutters cutting it to length. Two or three sizes of pliers should be stocked, with at least one pair of long-nosed pliers. Pliers should not be used as a substitute for spanners, and a set of small spanners, though not listed for the C & G 224 set, will be very useful. Long-nosed pliers should not be used for unscrewing inaccessible nuts, because this is one almost certain way of twisting the jaws of these pliers. The correct solution for such problems is a set of long tubular (box) spanners in the old BA sizes along with some of the smaller metric sizes.

Wire-cutters are usually of the popular side-cutter type. These have to be used with care on some types of wire, because the cut fragments will fly from the cutters at high speed and are a hazard to the eyes. The older 'nipper' type of wire-cutter is safer in this respect, and one pair should be carried along with the side-cutters.

Wire-strippers should be easily adjustable – if the adjustment is clumsy or time-consuming there will always be a temptation to try to judge the depth of stripping rather than setting it correctly. Taking a deep bite into a wire in order to strip the insulation will weaken the wire badly, and can be a cause of later failure, particularly on circuitry that is subject to vibration. The insulated wire to be stripped should be held in pliers while the strippers are being used. Both strippers and wire-cutters should be replaced if they become blunt or if the blades of cutters become damaged.

Hacksaws used for electronics work can be of the 'junior' size, with perhaps one larger hacksaw reserved for heavier work. A good selection of blades is necessary, because different blades are needed for steel, aluminium and SRBP. The blade must be correctly fitted, with the teeth pointing away from the handle so that the cutting stroke is when the saw is moving away from you. The blade must also be correctly tensioned. A slack blade is likely to twist and snap, and this is a hazard because the snapped blades have very sharp edges.

The work should always be securely clamped, and the saw should be held in both hands, one on the handle and one at the front of the saw-frame. Blades should be discarded whenever they are blunt or if they lose a tooth. Blades should be kept in packs so that the different blades can easily be distinguished.

Crimping tools are used to make solderless connections to cables by way of crimped connectors ('crimps') which are compressed on to the wire of a cable. Never use pliers as a substitute for the correct type of tool, because pliers will

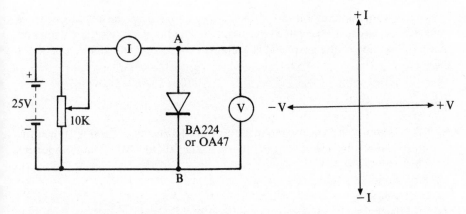

Figure 5.26   Diagram for Exercise 5.3

flatten the crimp rather than close it evenly around the wire. Crimping tools are specialized, and some are not suitable for uninsulated crimps; others are unsuitable for push-on connectors. A good compromise is one combination crimper for both insulated and uninsulated connectors, and a ratchet type for use with insulated crimps.

Marking-out tools are used to mark lines for cutting by hacksaw or for drilling. The scriber is used for marking lines for cutting, and the centre-punch for marking a hole position. A centre-punch should *always* be used before drilling so as to ensure that the drill will not run off position. Never use the centre-punch as a scriber, however. The scriber should be used in conjunction with a metal ruler for straight lines; for circles a compass-scriber can be used. Scribers are sharp, and should be kept in a holder when not in use so that the point is covered. Centre punches should also be kept out of the way. When using the centre punch, the work needs to be laid on a hard surface, preferably a metal block. Use of a centre-punch on a soft surface can result in an indentation that is much too large, deforming the metal.

Exercise 5.3
Construct the circuit shown in Figure 5.26 using either of the general-purpose diodes. Make sure that you know which end of the diode is the cathode. The voltmeter should be set to a low range, preferably 0–1 or 0–1.5 V, and the current meter to a 20 or 25 mA range. Start with the potentiometer in the position which will supply zero voltage. If you are uncertain of this, always remove the diode before switching on.

Plot several values of V and I for the diode connected as shown. Plot values of V in the range 0–0.6V even though no current is indicated, and for several values of voltage up to a current of about 20 mA. These values should be plotted on the +I, +V side of the graph as shown.

95

Now reverse the connection of the diode, and repeat the readings – it is unlikely that any readable value of current will be obtained. Plot these values on the $-I$, $-V$ side of the graph. This graph is now a complete characteristic for the diode.

Test questions

5.1 A continuity test on a component produced a reading of 500 K. When the test leads were interchanged, the reading fell to 50Ω. The component tested was a
   (a) diode
   (b) capacitor
   (c) thermistor
   (d) voltage dependent resistor.

5.2 A current flowing along a conductor produces a
   (a) chemical effect only
   (b) heating effect only
   (c) magnetic effect only
   (d) both heating and magnetic effects.

5.3 A circuit constructed entirely from passive components
   (a) increases signal amplitude
   (b) decreases signal amplitude
   (c) reduces signal distortion
   (d) causes signal inversion.

5.4 A series circuit consisting of a resistor and capacitor will
   (a) block a.c. and d.c.
   (b) pass a.c. and d.c.
   (c) pass a.c. only
   (d) pass d.c. only

5.5 A European manufactured silicon transistor would have a reference code that starts with
   (a) 2N
   (b) A
   (c) B
   (d) C

5.6 The most suitable instrument for measuring d.c. voltages in a high impedance circuit is
   (a) a moving coil meter
   (b) a moving iron meter
   (c) a potentiometer
   (d) an electronic meter.

6   Capacitance and capacitors

Refer to syllabus section 07(004)

A simple capacitor can be made by using two conducting plates separated from one another by a gap. When such an arrangement is connected by a battery, a current flows for a very short time, but then dies down to zero. The action of the battery has been to pump electrons from one of the plates on to the other until the latter is so negatively charged that it will take no more. It is the 'pumping' action which is detectable as current flow.

If the capacitor be now disconnected from the battery, the electrons which have been moved from one of its plates to the other will still remain out of place, but would return to the more positive plate through any conducting path. This return passage will cause another current to flow.

The capacitor as it is disconnected from the battery is said to be *charged*. The amount of charge stored is related to the voltage of the battery (or other supply) which is used to do the charging, and to another quantity called *capacitance* which is a measure of the ability of the capacitor to store electric charge (electrons).

As a capacitor is charged, the ratio of the charge transferred beween the plates to the voltage across the plates remains constant. In symbols, $C = Q/V$, where Q is the charge measured in coulombs and V the voltage in volts. The constant C is the capacitance. It is measured in *farads* (F) when the other units are quoted in terms of coulombs and volts.

The coulomb is a very large unit – the amount of charge carried by

6.28×10^{18} electrons and so the farad is also a very large unit. For this reason, sub-divisions of the farad – the *microfarad* (μF), the *nanofarad* (nF) and the *picofarad* (pF) are much used in electronic work. One μF = 10^{-6}F (one millionth of a farad), and 1nF = 10^{-3}μF (one thousandth of a microfarad). The pF is one thousandth of the nanofarad, and thus one millionth of the μF. In figures, 1pF = 10^{-12}F.

The value of the capacitance which can be achieved by the arrangement of two parallel conductors depends on three factors: (a) the *effective dimensions* of the conductors, (b) the *distance they are apart*, and (c) the nature of the insulating material (or *dielectric*) which is used to separate them. These factors affect the capacitance value in the following ways:

(a) Capacitance is *proportional to the area of overlap of the conductors* – their 'effective area' for purposes of capacitance (see Figure 6.2). The greater the area of overlap, the greater the capacitance. Some types of capacitor acquire comparatively large values of capacitance by using conductors in the form of strips which can be wound into rolls, so that a large amount of capacitive area is achieved in a small space.

(b) Capacitance is *inversely proportional to the spacing between the conducting plates*. This means that, for a given pair of plates, a reduction in the distance between them increases their value of capacitance. High-value capacitors therefore need insulators which are as thin as possible. Thin insulators, however, are easily broken down if the voltage across them is too high. Every capacitor therefore carries a maximum voltage rating, which must not be exceeded. Failure of the insulating material in a capacitor is called *dielectric breakdown*. It results in the failure of the capacitor, often producing a short circuit between the terminals.

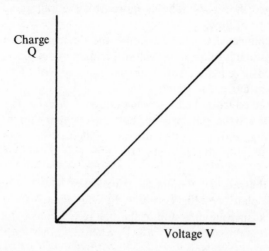

$\frac{Q}{V}$ = Capacitance C

Figure 6.1   Charge, voltage and capacitance

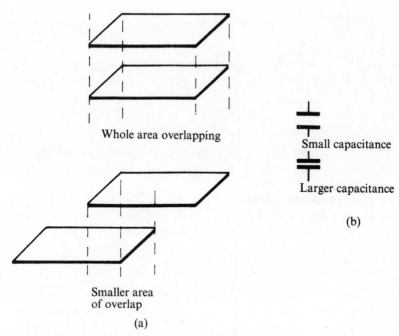

Whole area overlapping

Small capacitance

Larger capacitance

(b)

Smaller area
of overlap

(a)

Figure 6.2 Capacitor plate overlap and spacing

(c) The nature of the material used as an insulator in a capacitor also contributes to its value of capacitance. The lowest values of capacitance between a given pair of plates are attained when the dielectric is merely air, or a vacuum; but materials such as waxed paper, plastics, mica and ceramics can increase the capacitance up to 25 times the value given by the same thickness of air or vacuum. This greater efficiency is caused by a property called the *relative permittivity* of the material.

The formula given in Figure 6.3 summarizes the three factors governing a capacitor's maximum value of capacitance.

Capacitor types

Many materials and methods of construction have been used to make capacitors, but only a few representative types can be usefully considered here.

Variable capacitors operate by putting to use the variation of capacitance value which is achieved when the area of overlap between the two plates of a capacitor is either increased or reduced, or when the spacing between the capacitor plates is altered. The commonly used multiple-plate variable capacitor has one set of blades fixed and an interleaving set mounted on a rotating shaft (see Figure 5.9). As the plates are more fully meshed, so the area of overlap

$$C = \frac{E_0 \times area}{spacing}$$

with area in square meters and spacing in meters.
If care is taken, the expression

$$C = \frac{E_0 A}{d}$$

with Am m^2 and dm mm can be used. This results in a value of C in units of pF if the value of 0.0088 is used for E_0

Figure 6.3 The capacitance formula

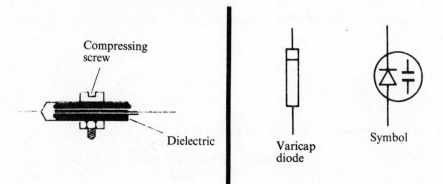

Compressing
screw

Dielectric

Varicap
diode

Symbol

Figure 6.4 A compression trimmer | **Figure 6.5 Varicap diode and symbol**

becomes greater and the value of capacitance is increased (and *vice versa*).

When the dielectric is air, quite a large component is needed to attain a maximum capacitance of even 500pF, so in miniature capacitors sheets of solid dielectric are placed between the plates. In so-called *compression trimmers* – see Figure 6.4 – most of which have a capacitance of some 50pF maximum, sprung plates are separated by dielectric sheets. An increase in capacitance is obtained by compressing the plates towards each other by means of a screw. Circuits using variable capacitors such as these are designed with the moving (adjustable) plates always at earth potential, so as to avoid the changes of capacitance which would otherwise occur when the control was touched (hand or body capacitance).

Another type of variable capacitor is the *varicap* diode (Figure 6.5) which is a semi-conductor diode whose capacitance is varied by changing the voltage across it.

Small capacitors of fixed value are simply constructed (see Figure 6.6), with the plate and the insulator arranged parallel to one another. Their insulators are

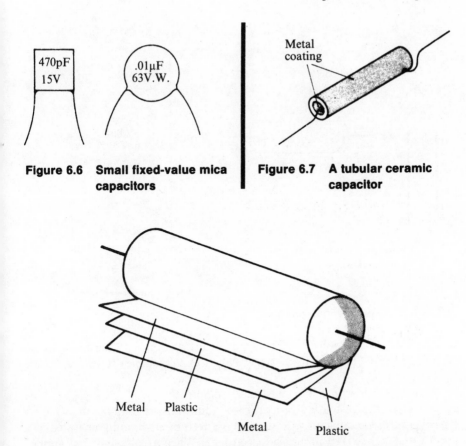

Figure 6.6　Small fixed-value mica capacitors

Figure 6.7　A tubular ceramic capacitor

Figure 6.8　The construction of a rolled plastic dielectric capacitor

often mica, which can also be silvered on both sides to form a silver-mica capacitor – a type chosen when stability of capacitance value is important. Thin sheets of ceramic are also much used. The complete capacitor, with lead-out wires attached, is then dipped in wax or plastic so as to insulate the plates and protect the assembly from moisture.

An alternative construction is the *tubular* type, in which the inside and outside surfaces of a ceramic tube are coated with metal to form a capacitor (Figure 6.7) This type is also coated in wax or plastic.

In wound or rolled capacitors, the conductors take the form of foil sheets. Typically, these are formed by evaporating metal on to both sides of a long strip of insulator, placing an insulating sheet along one of the sides to prevent short circuits, and then rolling the whole assembly up like a Swiss roll. Separate metal foils can also be rolled together in this way, as shown in Figure 6.8. The insulators are either waxed paper or plastics of various kinds, such as polycar-

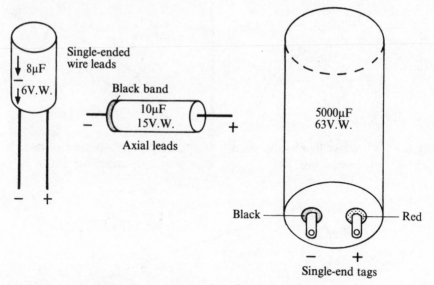

Figure 6.9 Electrolytic capacitors

bonate, polythene or polyester. This type of construction can be used for values of 1nF to 1μF or more, but for larger values of capacitance rolled capacitors tend to get bulky.

Electrolytic capacitors are constructed differently (see Figure 6.9), taking advantage of the insulating properties of thin films of aluminium oxide. A typical electrolytic capacitor is composed of sheets of aluminium separated by a porous material soaked in an acid electrolyte. When a voltage is first applied across the plates – a process which is called *forming* – a current flows briefly until one plate is covered with an invisibly thin film of aluminium oxide. This film is a good insulator, and since it is thinner than any other usable solid material, very large values of capacitance can be attained by using it. In addition, the area of the foil can be greatly increased by corrugating it or, better still, by etching it to a rough finish. The voltage which can be applied across the film is, however, limited; and it *must* be applied in the correct polarity.

One of the terminals of an electrolytic capacitor is marked (+), the other (−); and this polarity must be observed. Connecting an electrolytic capacitor the wrong way round would cause the oxide film to be broken down, and large currents would flow. This could cause the casing to burst, spraying both the operator and the rest of the circuit with corrosive material. Electrolytic capacitors used to smooth power supplies are particularly at risk in this respect, for very large currents would flow in the event of an internal short-circuit.

Electrolytic capacitors, in addition to their applications with power supplies – see Chapter 11 – are used as coupling and de-coupling capacitors in a.f. circuits,

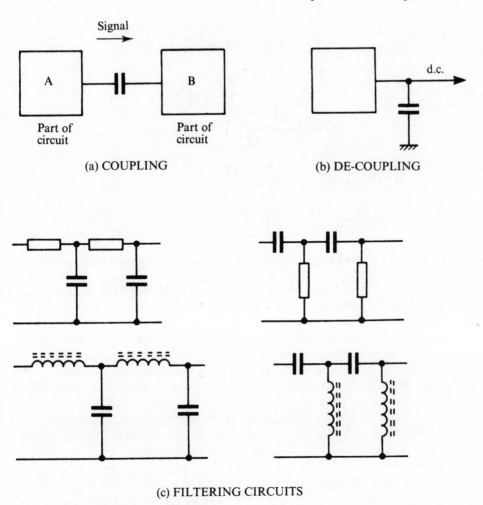

(a) COUPLING

(b) DE-COUPLING

(c) FILTERING CIRCUITS

Figure 6.10   Capacitor applications

see Figure 6.10. In either role, the capacitor allows a.c. signal currents to pass freely, even if signal frequency is low, while preventing the passage of all but a very small d.c. leakage current. In some applications, this d.c. leakage current is undesirable, and capacitors of a different construction must be used.

For this purpose, a useful alternative is the *tantalum electrolytic*, which permits much less leakage current – but which is a much more expensive component. Tantalum electrolytics, unlike the aluminium variety, can be obtained in either polarized or unpolarized form.

Wound capacitors with values in the range 1nF to 1μF are used in audio coupling, de-coupling and filtering, in r.f. de-coupling and in low-frequency

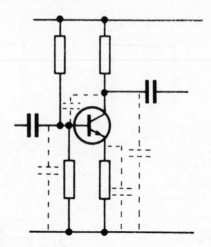

Figure 6.11 Stray capacitances can be significant at high frequencies

oscillators. Ceramic capacitors are used in r.f. de-coupling, and silver mica capacitors in r.f. tuned circuits. Variable capacitors are used in oscillator, tuned-amplifier and tuned filter circuits.

In addition to any capacitors which may be deliberately placed in a circuit, there often exists between any two parts of a circuit, physically close to one another but not connected, what is called a *stray capacitance* – 'stray' in this sense meaning unintentional. When the signals being handled by the circuit are of low frequency, this stray capacitance is of little importance; but things can be very different in circuits working at high frequencies. If, for instance, the circuit shown in Figure 6.11 were required to handle high-frequency signals, undesirable stray capacitances could be set up between the parts of the circuit indicated by dotted lines.

Stray capacitances can often be minimized by careful layout of a circuit, but there is always an unavoidable stray capacitance across each individual component and this amount is not reduced by altering layout.

Screening

Screening is a method which makes indirect use of the effects of stray capacitance to shield one part of a circuit from signals radiated by another part. An electrostatic screen removes unwanted signals which could be passed by stray capacitances by enclosing the circuit which could be affected in an earthed metal box. This box need not be solid. Any stray signal current reaching the box returns to earth through the metal casing, and is so prevented from affecting the circuits being screened.

Note that a different form of screening is needed for magnetic signals. It is

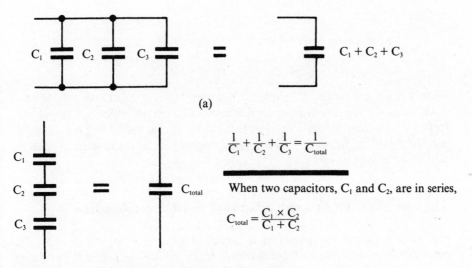

Figure 6.12   Capacitors in parallel and in series

described in Chapter 12.

Capacitors in combination

Capacitors, like resistors, can be connected in series, in parallel or in series-parallel combinations. Whatever the method of connection, any combination of capacitors can be 'replaced' by a single capacitor of equivalent value. The size of this equivalent capacitance can be calculated from first principles. It is equal to the total charge stored by the capacitor network, divided by the total voltage across the network.

This method of calculation must be employed in complex capacitor circuits, but simple formulae can be used to calculate the resultant capacitance when capacitors are connected either wholly in series or wholly in parallel (see Figure 6.12).

When capacitors are connected *in parallel*, their equivalent value is found by *adding their individual values of capacitance*. Thus

$$C_{total} = C_1 + C_2 + C_3 + \ldots\ldots$$

When capacitors are connected *in series*, their equivalent value is found by *adding the inverses of their individual values of capacitance*. Thus

$$\frac{1}{C_{total}} = \frac{1}{C_1} + \frac{1}{C_2} + \frac{1}{C_3} + \ldots\ldots$$

or for two capacitors

$$C_{total} = \frac{C_1 C_2}{C_1 + C_2}$$

Note that these formulae for capacitors in combination are at first sight similar to those governing resistors in combination. The crucial difference is that the formula for adding *resistors in series* is the same as that for adding *capacitors in parallel*, while the formula for adding *resistors in parallel* is the same as that for adding *capacitors in series*.

The time constant of a capacitor-and-resistor combination

The voltage across the plates of a capacitor rises as charge flows into the capacitor from a source such as a battery. When the voltage across the plates of the capacitor is equal to the battery voltage, charge cannot continue to flow because there is no voltage difference to cause electrons to move. The capacitor is now completely charged.

When the charging circuit embodies a resistor, the rate of movement of charge (electron flow) is reduced. 'Rate of movement of charge' is but another name for 'current flow', and the presence of a resistor in the circuit could be expected to reduce current flow by the terms of Ohm's Law. Adding more resistance to a capacitor-charging circuit therefore increases the time needed to charge the capacitor.

Conversely, if the capacitor is disconnected from the power supply and a resistor is connected in parallel with it, charge will return through the resistor until the capacitor is discharged again, with no voltage difference remaining between the plates. The presence of the resistor will, however, slow down the rate of discharge of the capacitor.

In practice, the charge/discharge process is normally so fast that a CRO is needed to observe the changing voltages across the capacitor plates.

A graph of voltage plotted against time for a charging capacitor is shown in Figure 6.13. This graph is an important one. Its shape is what is called *exponential* – and the notable feature about it is the way in which the graph flattens out as the plates of the capacitor approach their final value of voltage difference. Because of this flattening-out effect, the final value of voltage is only gradually approached, with the last percent of the charge taking a relatively long time to get on to the plate.

In other words, the capacitor is *almost* charged a relatively long time before it is *fully* charged, and the last few percent of its full charge are relatively unimportant in measuring its effective capacity.

For this reason, a concept called the *time constant* of the capacitor–resistor

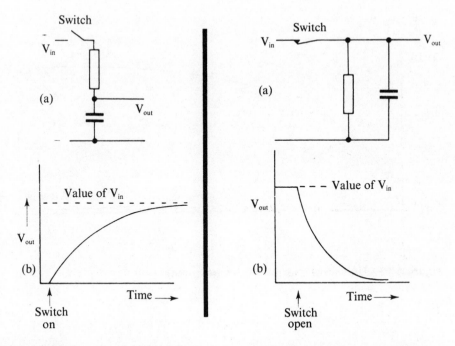

Figure 6.13   Capacitor charging   **Figure 6.14   Capacitor discharging**

combination is used as a measure of the length of time which the capacitor needs to be charged to within this last few percent of its final value of charge. This being so, it is not surprising that the time constant is calculated in terms of $R \times C$. When R is quoted in ohms and C in farads, the quantity RC will be given in units of seconds of time. When, as is more usual, it is measured in kilohms (k) and C in nF, the time constant is given in microseconds (µs).

The significance of time constant is that charging or discharging is about 63 per cent complete after the elapse of one time constant. After a period of four time constants, charging is more than 98 per cent complete.

Figure 6.14 shows the effect of capacitor discharge in a circuit. It will be seen that the graph is still exponential (though the other way up). The same comments about the practical value of a time constant therefore apply to capacitor discharge as they did to charge, with the charge reduced to 37 per cent of its initial value after one time constant, and to about 2 per cent of its initial value after four time constants.

Figure 6.15 shows universal charge/discharge curves which enable the voltage of a charging or discharging capacitor to be read off the chart in terms of the capacitor's time constant and maximum voltage.

The importance of these charging and discharging time constants is, as you will see in Chapter 7, that they can be used in two forms of wave-shaping

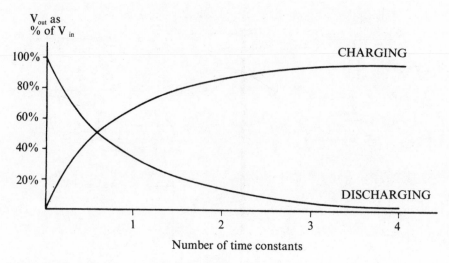

Figure 6.15   Universal charge/discharge curves

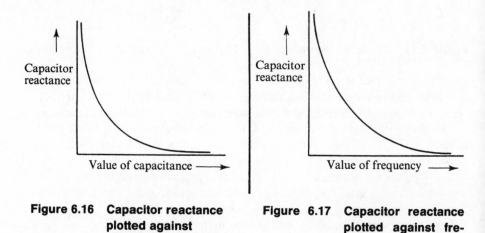

Figure 6.16   Capacitor reactance plotted against capacitor value fixed frequency

Figure 6.17   Capacitor reactance plotted against frequency fixed capacitor value

operations known as *differentiation* and *integration*, which can be performed by resistor-capacitor networks of the type described.

At signal frequencies, capacitors permit signal current to flow when a signal voltage exists between the plates. The ratio of signal voltage to signal current is called the *reactance* (X_C) of the capacitor, and is measured in ohms. Figure 6.16 shows a graph of capacitor reactance plotted against capacitance, for a constant frequency of signal; while Figure 6.17 shows a graph of capacitor reactance plotted against frequency, for a constant value of capacitance.

It will be seen that the reactance of a capacitor is lower for large values of capacitance than it is for small values, and is also lower at high frequencies than it is at low frequencies.

Test questions

6.1 Two metal plates are insulated from each other. The capacitance between them will increase if the
(a) plates are brought closer
(b) plates are moved further apart
(c) area of the plates is reduced
(d) insulation is removed.

6.2 A 1 farad capacitor is found to have a potential of 10 volts across its terminals. The charge on the capacitor is
(a) 0.1 coulombs
(b) 1 coulomb
(c) 10 coulombs
(d) 100 coulombs.

6.3 A d.c. voltage applied to an electrolytic capacitor must be
(a) accompanied by a.c.
(b) of correct polarity and voltage
(c) of correct polarity and any voltage
(d) of correct voltage and any polarity.

6.4 Total capacitance is increased when capacitors are connected in
(a) bridge form
(b) series
(c) series parallel
(d) parallel.

6.5. The reactance of a capacitor to a signal frequency will be large if the capacitance is
(a) small and the frequency is high
(b) large and the frequency is high
(c) large and the frequency is low
(d) small and the frequency is low

6.6 The time constant of a resistor/capacitor combination measures the
(a) charging current
(b) current at 37 per cent of full voltage
(c) time to charge to 63 per cent of final voltage
(d) time to charge to 37 per cent of final voltage.

7 Waveforms, filters and wave-shaping circuits

Refer to syllabus section 04 (004, 4.5)

A *block diagram* of an electronic circuit is used to show *what the circuit does* rather than how it does it. It simplifies fault diagnosis, because the general area of the circuit in which a fault is to be looked for is often easier to diagnose from a block diagram than it is from a full and much more complex circuit diagram. (In addition, many systems using ICs have only block diagrams.)

Another reason for the use of a block diagram is that the full circuit diagrams of some electronic devices, such as colour TV receivers and particularly computers, are far too large and complex to draw on a single sheet of paper. The circuit is therefore divided into blocks, with one sheet of paper showing the full circuit diagram of one block, with all (or most) of the components and connections drawn in. The relation of each of these blocks to one another is then indicated on a full block diagram of the device as a whole.

Block diagrams are also used to show the waveforms which ought to be present at various points in a circuit. The waveforms present at most points in a circuit can be made visible with the aid of a cathode ray oscilloscope (CRO). Any significant deformation in the shape or amplitude of a waveform often indicates a fault in that particular part of the circuit.

Both block diagrams and waveforms showing typical signals will be used throughout this book. Their purpose and use should be thoroughly understood at this stage.

110

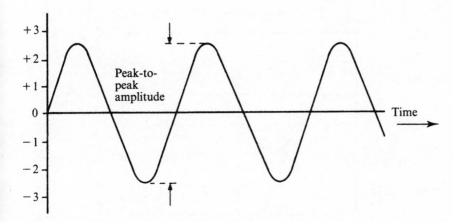

Figure 7.1   Peak-to-peak amplitude shown on a graph

Waveform measurements

A waveform is best represented by a graph of a wave quantity (either voltage or current) plotted against time, as was seen in Chapter 3. The same waveform should also be seen when a CRO is applied to the correct point in a circuit, and measurements of waveform quantities (or *parameters*) at that point can be made. The most useful measurements are generally those of wave amplitude and time period (or wave *duration*).

The *amplitude* of a waveform is a measure of the total amount by which the voltage (or current) varies during one cycle of a wave. The *peak-to-peak amplitude* of a wave is shown in Figure 7.1, but is more easily measured on the face of a CRO tube (Figure 7.2) where it is found by measuring the vertical distance in centimetres between peaks of the wave and then multiplying this distance by the settings of the 'Volts/cm' switch of the oscilloscope. For example, a peak-to-peak (p-p) distance of 3cm at a setting of 5V/cm corresponds to (3x5V =) 15V p-p.

On a graph, the p-p amplitude can be read from the calibrated vertical scale of the graph.

Peak amplitude alone – as opposed to peak-to-peak amplitude – is sometimes measured when the waveform is symmetrical. A symmetrical waveform has exactly the same shape above and below its centre line. Figure 7.3 shows a *sine-wave* (which is always symmetrical) and a *square wave* (which is not always symmetrical, but here is).

Meters which are used to read values of wave amplitude do not record the peak-to-peak amplitude. A meter set on its d.c. voltage (or current) range will read the *average* value of voltage or current flow – which means the value of the net d.c. voltage current flowing, or the *average* value of the flow of unidirectio-

111

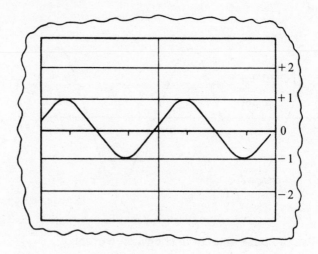

Figure 7.2   Peak-to-peak amplitude measured on an oscilloscope

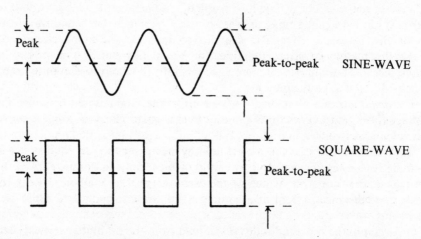

Figure 7.3   Peak amplitude and peak-to-peak amplitude on symmetrical waveforms

nal current. The scale, however, will indicate the equivalent root mean square (r.m.s.) value. A waveform will show (Figure 7.4) an average value of current flow in one direction if the *area* of the graph of the wave above (or below) the centre-line of the graph is greater than the area of the graph of the wave in the other direction.

When a mixture of d.c. and a.c. is present in a circuit, this *average value* shows the amount of d.c. present.

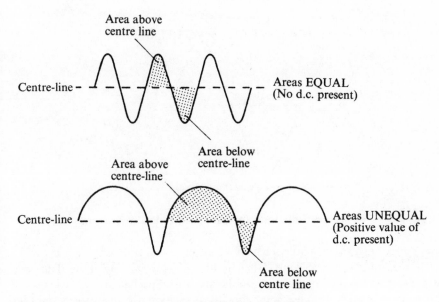

Figure 7.4   The d.c. component of differing waveforms

Another method of measuring amplitude is used mainly with sine-waves. It is called the *root mean square*, or *r.m.s.* When a sine-wave is said to have a value of current flow of 1A r.m.s., it means that it will produce the same amount of power dissipation in a resistor as will a steady d.c. current of 1A. Equally, 1V r.m.s. applied across a resistor will produce the same amount of power dissipation as will one volt of d.c.

When a waveform of a.c. is a sine-wave, the r.m.s. value of its amplitude will be *0.707 times its peak value* (or *peak value divided by the square root of 2*).

Other waveforms have different relationships between their r.m.s. and peak values; so meter readings of r.m.s. voltages and currents should be taken *only* when sine-waves are being measured. Some specialized instruments exist which measure the r.m.s. value of *any* waveform; but you will not find them *much* used in servicing applications.

The *periodic time* (or *duration*) of a waveform is another important quantity which can be measured by using an oscilloscope, or which can be read from a graph. The period of a wave is the time taken for a complete cycle of the wave, as indicated in Figure 7.5.

To measure this quantity on the CRO display, the waveform must be *synchronized* or *locked* — which means that the display must not be moving across the screen. The distance in cm between corresponding points is then measured. The 'corresponding points' may be either the positive or the negative peaks, or the zero voltage levels at the points where the voltage is changing in the same

113

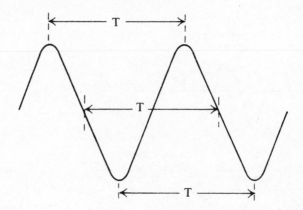

Figure 7.5   T is the periodic time (or duration) of the waveform

direction, or any other features which repeat once and once only, per cycle.

The measured distance in cm is then multiplied by the setting of the 'Time/cm' switch to give the time period in seconds, ms or μs. Special care is needed when this reading is taken because some models of oscilloscope incorporate *potentiometer control* of time/cm, in addition to the switch. It is necessary for this potentiometer to be set to one end of its travel before the time reading is taken.

The *frequency* of a wave is the number of complete cycles of the wave accomplished per second. It is thus equal to 1/Period. If the period is measured in seconds, 1/Period gives the frequency in units of *hertz* (Hz), or cycles per second. If the period is measured in milliseconds (ms), the frequency value will be in *kilohertz* (kHz). If the period is measured in microseconds (μs) the frequency value will be in *Megahertz* (MHz).

The frequencies used in electronics are often identified by their *range of value* rather than by quoting exact frequencies. Thus the expression *low frequency (l.f.)* covers all frequencies below 50Hz extending right down to d.c. *Audio frequency (a.f.)* covers the range of frequencies from about 40Hz to 20kHz – which is about the range of sound wave frequencies which can be detected by the younger human ear.

Frequencies higher than the audio range are collectively known as *radio frequencies* (R.F.), but certain ranges of R.F. have distinctive names. Thus the range 460 kHz to 470 kHz is called *intermediate frequency* (I.F.) because of its special use in AM superhet receivers (see Chapter 9). Frequencies in the range 30 MHz to about 300 MHz are called *very high frequency* VHF, and frequencies above about 300 MHz *ultra-high-frequency* (UHF).

All these names are purely matters of convenience, lacking precise definitions. For example, frequencies of 100 kHz or so can generally be handled by the same circuits as are used for audio frequencies. Such frequencies could logically, therefore, be classified as 'audio frequencies', even though a 100 kHz sound

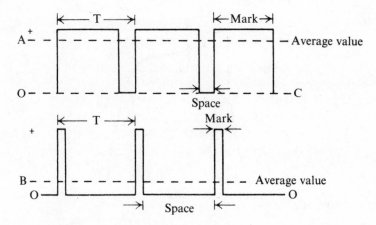

Figure 7.6 Rectangular waveforms or pulses

wave cannot be heard by any human ear. It is thus an *ultrasonic* frequency – which means that it lies beyond the frequency range which the human ear is capable of detecting.

Rectangular waves, shown in Figure 7.6, require an additional measurement. It is called their *mark-to-space ratio*. It is perfectly possible for two rectangular waves of the same period (and therefore of the same frequency) to have quite different shapes, and also quite different values of average voltage. In a rectangular wave, therefore, the *mark* is taken as the length of time for which the voltage is positive and the *space* as the length of time for which the wave is either at zero or at a negative voltage. A wave with a large mark-to-space ratio will thus have an average value nearly equal to its positive peak value, while a wave with a small mark-to-space ratio will have an average value nearly equal to its negative peak value (i.e., in the example shown in Figure 7.6, nearly equal to zero).

Varying the mark-to-space ratio of a rectangular wave of voltage is often used as a method of motor speed control.

Other parameters of a square wave which can be measured with the aid of an oscilloscope are its *rise* and *fall times*, its *sag* and its *overshoot* voltages. All are illustrated in Figure 7.7. The rise and fall times are, respectively, the times taken for the voltage to rise (fall) between its 10 per cent and its 90 per cent voltage levels, or *vice versa*. Overshoot is the minor initial jump of voltage by which the leading edge of the square wave often exceeds the nominal peak level of the wave; while sag is the extent to which the peak voltage drops below nominal peak level before the trailing edge of the waveform arrives.

The *wavelength* of a wave is a quantity which applies only to a wave travelling in space or along a wire. It can be measured easily only when the wavelength is short, and is defined as *the closest distance between neighbouring points at which*

115

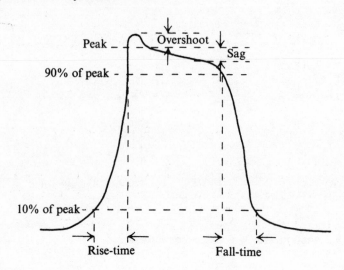

Figure 7.7   Imperfections in a rectangular pulse

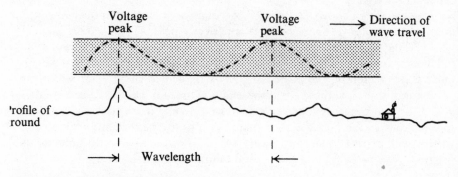

Figure 7.8   The wavelength of a transmitted wave

the voltage to which the wave gives rise reaches an identical peak. The concept is illustrated in Figure 7.8.

These points of closest distances are called *antinodes*. They can sometimes be located on wires with the aid of lamp indicators (see Figure 7.9); but the wavelength of a wave is generally a calculated quantity. The formula used is:

$$\lambda = \frac{c}{f}$$

where

λ is the wavelength in metres
c the speed of wave travel in metres per second
f the frequency of wave in Hz.

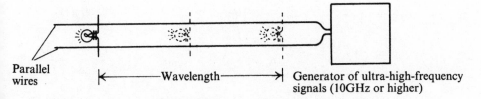

Parallel
wires ⊢←———————Wavelength————————→⊣ Generator of ultra-high-frequency
signals (10GHz or higher)

Figure 7.9   Measuring the wavelengths of UHF waves travelling along wires

The symbol λ, is the Greek letter *lambda* (English L).

In free space, the speed of all radio waves is identical at 3×10^8 metres per second. (10^8 is the figure 1 followed by eight zeros, so 3×10^8 is 300 million). By comparison, the speed of sound in still air is about 332 m/s, but this is affected by movement of the air or by movement of the source of the sound. We can write the relationship as

$$\frac{c}{\lambda f}$$

using the triangle as a reminder of the three possible forms of the equation

$$c = \lambda f \qquad \lambda = c/f \qquad f = c/\lambda$$

Wavelength calculations are of particular importance in the design and use of aerials for high-frequency (mainly TV) signals.

Examples:
What are the wavelengths, in free space, of waves of the following frequencies:

    (a) 1 MHz?   (b) 30 MHz?   (c) 900 MHz?

Solution: Use the equations $\lambda = \dfrac{c}{f}$ and $c = 3 \times 10^8$ m/s. Then

(a) 1 MHz is 10^6 Hz. So $\lambda = \dfrac{3 \times 10^8}{10^6} = 3 \times 10^2 = 300$ metres.

(b) 30 MHz is 3×10^7 Hz. So $\lambda = \dfrac{3 \times 10^8}{3 \times 10^7} = 10$ metres.

(c) 900 MHz is 9×10^8 Hz. So $\lambda = \dfrac{3 \times 10^8}{9 \times 10^8} =$ one third of a metre, or 33.3 cm.

A wave may be either pure a.c. or unidirectional. A pure a.c. wave, of course, has an average value of zero, so it can cause no deflection of a d.c. meter. A wave fed through a capacitor or derived from the secondary of a transformer (see Figure 7.10) is always of this type – apart from certain short-lived (*transient*) effects which occur immediately after the circuit is switched on.

A uni-directional wave is one having a steady average value which can be measured by a d.c. meter. Such a wave has a *d.c. component*, which means that its amplitude must be measured by a d.c. meter. The *a.c. component* of the same

117

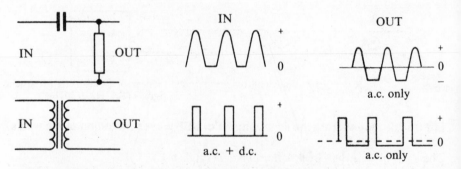

Figure 7.10   Circuits which transmit no d.c. component

wave can also be measured when the d.c. component is absent, by inserting a capacitor (which may have to be of large value) between the circuit and the a.c. meter. This assumes that a suitable a.c. meter is obtainable. Most a.c. meters will give correct readings only for sinusoidal waveforms.

Harmonics

A sine-wave has a single value of frequency, but waves which are not of sine-wave shape (*non-sinusoidal waves*) contain other frequencies, called *harmonics*. An instrument known as a spectrum analyser can detect what frequencies are present in such waves.

One frequency, called the *fundamental frequency*, is always present. It is the frequency equal to 1/Period for the waveform. No frequencies of less than this fundamental value can exist for a given wave, but higher frequencies which are whole-number multiples of the fundamental frequency (i.e., twice, three times its value and so on) are often present. When this is so, the amplitude of these 'harmonic' waves will have an effect on the shape of the total waveform. Figure 7.11 shows the wave-shapes which result from adding (a) the 3rd and 5th harmonics to a sine wave, and (b) the odd harmonics up to the 15th. The higher harmonics generally have small amplitudes, so that very high harmonics have little effect on the wave-shape.

Note that rectangular waves contain high proportions of odd-numbered harmonics 3,5,7,9 . . . .), while triangular and sawtooth waveforms (see Figure 7.12) contain high proportions of the even-numbered harmonics.

The principle of wave analysis is important as a method of measuring amplifier distortion. A perfect sine-wave signal applied to the input of an amplifier will produce a perfect sine-wave output only if the amplifier causes no distortion. Any alteration in the wave-shape brought about by distortion will cause harmonics to be present in the output signal. These harmonics can be isolated

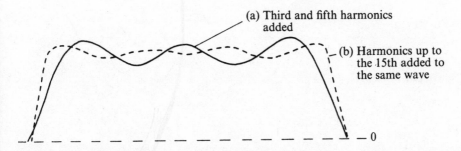

(a) Third and fifth harmonics
added

(b) Harmonics up to
the 15th added to
the same wave

— 0

Figure 7.11   Wave-shapes produced by adding harmonics to the fundamental frequency of a sine wave

Triangular
wave

Sawtooth
wave

Figure 7.12   Triangular and sawtooth waveforms

and measured to enable the amount of the distortion which has taken place to be quantified.

Filters

Filters are circuits which act on waveforms to change both their amplitude and their phase. So-called *passive* filter circuits (which consist wholly of passive components) will never increase the amplitude of a wave but will either reduce it or leave it unchanged. The gain produced by such a filter, in other words, is the quantity:

$$\frac{\text{Amplitude of output wave}}{\text{Amplitude of input wave}}$$

when the result is unity or less.

Filter circuits do not change the shape of sine-waves, but they do alter the shapes of other waveforms (see later in this chapter).

119

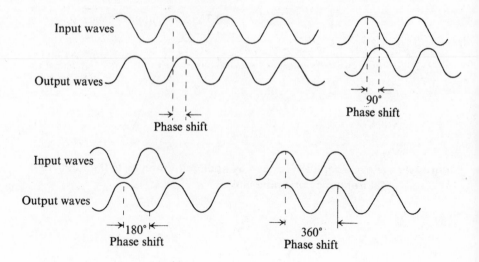

Input waves

Output waves

Phase shift

90°
Phase shift

Input waves

Output waves

180°
Phase shift

360°
Phase shift

Figure 7.13   Phase shift

Many filter circuits cause the phase of a sine-wave to shift. This means that the peak of the waveform at the output does not occur at the same time as the peak of the wave at the input (see Figure. 7.13). *Phase shift* is measured in degrees, with 360° representing one complete cycle of difference between input and output waves. On this scale, 180° represents half a cycle of difference, and 90° a quarter of a cycle.

A double-beam oscilloscope, which uses two separate Y (vertical deflection) amplifiers and a common timebase to control two CRT beams, can be made to show phase shift by displaying both input and output waveforms on the same timebase. When the time difference t between the waves is measured, the phase shift is given in degrees by the expression: t/T × 360°, where T is the time period or duration of a complete cycle of the waveform.

Example: The time difference between the peaks of two sets of waves is 10μs, and the wave period of each is 50μs. What phase-shift has occurred, in degrees?

Solution: Substitute the data in the equation t/T × 360°.

$$\text{Then } \frac{10}{50} \times 360° = 72°$$

Wave filters can be designed to cope with waves of any range of frequencies from low (a few Hz only) to high radio frequencies of many hundreds of MHz. The components and circuit design of the filters vary considerably according to the frequency range they are designed to handle.

Whatever the range of frequencies handled by a filter, however, the main filter types are *low-pass, high-pass, band-pass* and *band-stop*. The symbols used in

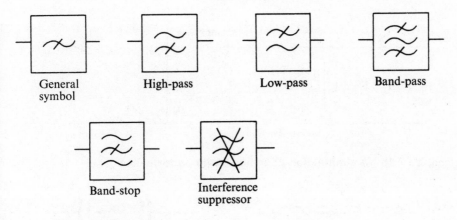

General
symbol
High-pass
Low-pass
Band-pass

Band-stop
Interference
suppressor

Figure 7.14   Filter symbols

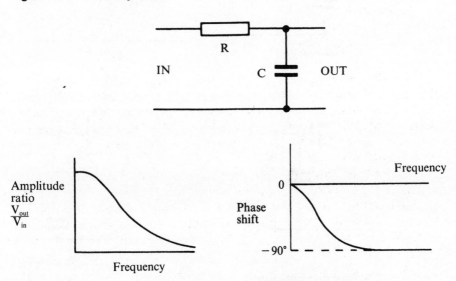

Figure 7.15   A simple low-pass filter and its performance graphs

block and circuit diagrams to indicate these types of filter action are shown in
Figure 7.14.

A low-pass filter, as its name suggests, passes without attenuation the low
frequencies of signals arriving at its input, but greatly reduces the amplitude of
high-frequency signals which are thereby heavily attenuated. Another way of
putting it is to say that a low-pass filter has a *pass-band* of low frequencies, but a
stop-band of high frequencies.

A simple form of low-pass filter is the RC filter shown in Figure 7.15 together
with typical performance graphs. These graphs show the variation of both gain

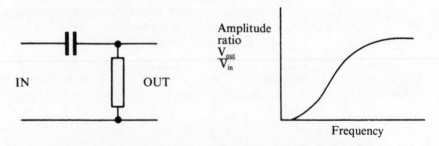

Figure 7.16   A simple high-pass filter, with performance graph

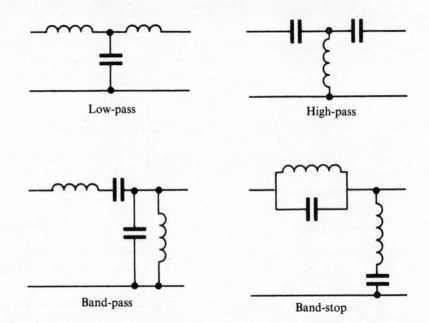

Figure 7.17   More complex filters

and phase plotted against frequency which the filter is capable of achieving.

Figure 7.16 shows a single CR high-pass filter with its measured gain/frequency performance graph.

Simple RC filters do not give sufficient attenuation for most purposes, and filters which include inductors as well as capacitors and resistors are also required. Both the theory and the practical design of such filters present difficulties, but Figure 7.17 illustrates examples of both low-pass and high-pass filters.

When inductors and capacitors are combined in a filter circuit, *band-pass* and *band-stop* filters can be constructed. Band-pass filters will pass a predetermined range of frequencies without attenuation, but will attenuate other frequencies both above and below this range. A band-stop filter has the opposite action, greatly reducing the amplitude of signals in a given band but having little effect on signals outside it.

A further type of filter, perhaps less frequently encountered, is the so-called *all-pass* filter. This type causes no attenuation of signals, but does bring about phase shifts from zero to 360°, over a wide range of frequencies.

Wave-shaping

The basic action of filter circuits on sine-waves is, as has been seen, to attenuate and change the phase of the waves but to leave the shape of the wave unaltered. When the input wave to a circuit is *not* a sine-wave, however, the action of even a passive circuit can change the shape of the wave considerably.

Circuits designed to change the shape of non-sinusoidal waves of this type are called *wave-shaping* circuits. If active components (that is to say, components other than capacitors, inductors and resistors) are included, the shapes of sine-waves themselves can also be changed.

Two important types of wave-shaping circuits are the *differentiating* circuit and the *integrating* circuit. A differentiating circuit is one which has an output only when the input wave changes amplitude. The amplitude of its output depends on how fast the amplitude of the input wave itself changes: the faster the change, the greater the output.

The normal differentiating circuit will act as a high-pass filter for sine waves. Its effect on a square wave is shown in Figure 7.18.

An integrating circuit removes sudden amplitude changes from a waveform, its effect being thus the opposite of that of the differentiating circuit. Integrating action on a square wave is shown in Figure 7.19. The circuit's action on a sine-wave is that of a low-pass filter.

When simple RC circuits are used for differentiating and integrating (see also Chapter 18), the circuit property called its *time constant* becomes important. It is measured by multiplying the value of R by the value of C. A *differentiating* circuit requires an RC time constant which is *small* compared with the wave period. An integrating circuit requires a time constant which is *large* compared with the wave period.

One result of these requirements is that differentiating or integrating circuits designed to handle a given wave frequency will have a different effect when a wave of either higher or lower frequency reaches them as an input.

The units in which the time constant is calculated must be strictly observed. If R and C are given in ohms and farads respectively, the time constant RC will appear in seconds. If (as is more likely) the units of R and C are given in kilohms and microfarads respectively, the constant RC will appear in milliseconds (ms). If R is in kilohms and C in nanofarads, RC will appear in microseconds (μs).

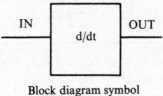

Block diagram symbol

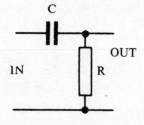

A simple differentiating circuit

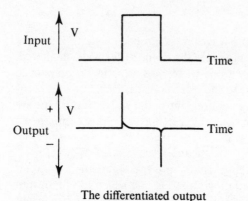

The differentiated output

Figure 7.18   Differentiation

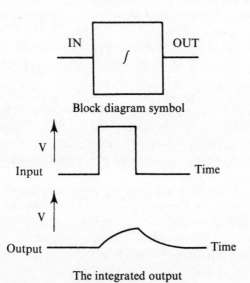

Block diagram symbol

The integrated output

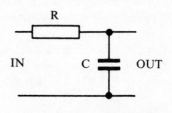

A simple integrating circuit

Figure 7.19   Integration

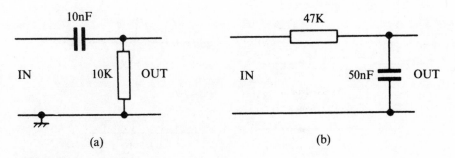

Figure 7.20 Diagrams for Exercise 7.1

Example: Calculate the time constants of
(a) 10k and .033µF
(b) 470R and 0.1µF
(c) 56k and 820 pF.

Solution:
(a) With R = 10k C must be converted into nanofarads. .033µF = 33nF.
The time constant is then 33 × 10 = 330µs.
(b) R must be converted into kilohms. 470R = 0.47k. With C = .1µF, the time constant is .47 × .1 = .047 ms, or 47µs.
(c) With R = 56k, C must again be converted into nanofarads. 820pF = 0.82nF.
The time constant is then 56 × .82 = 45.9µs, or about 46µs.

Save in a few low-frequency circuits, the unit of microseconds is the most convenient for use in time constant calculations.

Exercise 7.1
Construct the wave-shaping circuit shown in Figure 7.20(a). Connect the oscilloscope to the output of the circuit and a square-wave signal generator to the input. Calculate the time constant for the circuit.

Now adjust the square-wave generator until it produces a wave of IV p-p at 1kHz. Sketch the output waveform from the wave-shaping circuit.

Set the generator to a frequency of 100 Hz and repeat the measurement.

Now carry out the same sequence of experiments on the wave-shaping circuit of Figure 7.20(b).

Repeat the experiment using 100 Hz and 1kHz sine waves and confirm that the only effect is alteration of phase shift.

Clipping, d.c. restoration and limiting circuits

Clipping, d.c. restoring and limiting are processes which can be carried out on waveforms of any shape, but which need components other than the resistors,

125

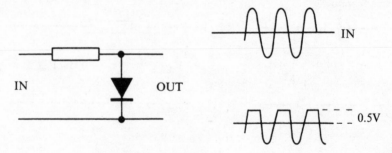

Figure 7.21   A simple clipping circuit

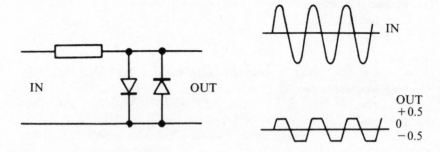

Figure 7.22   Two-way clipping

capacitors and inductors used in wave filters.

Clipping means the removal of part of either peak of a wave. A simple clipping circuit is shown in Figure 7.21. The silicon diode does not conduct when its anode is negative, and will conduct only when its anode voltage reaches about 0.5V positive.

The clipping circuit as a whole acts like a potential divider, with the diode resistance being very high for voltages of less than 0.5V. The waveform is therefore clipped at +0.5V.

Such a clipped waveform will have a d.c. component unless both positive and negative peaks are clipped equally. A circuit for doing this is shown in Figure 7.22.

Restoration (or *d.c. restoration*) is the process of restoring to a signal the d.c. level which it will have lost if it has been passed through a capacitor or a transformer. Figure 7.23 shows a typical application.

The unidirectional waveform is amplified and passed through a capacitor, so losing its d.c. component (a). A simple d.c. restoring circuit (b) then replaces the missing d.c. – a typical such circuit is shown – and (c) the d.c. level is again present.

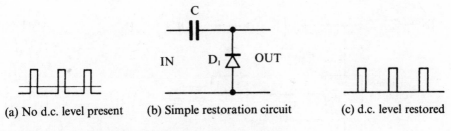

(a) No d.c. level present   (b) Simple restoration circuit   (c) d.c. level restored

Figure 7.23   How a d.c. restoration circuit works

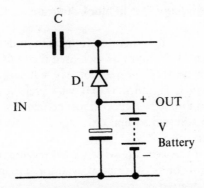

Figure 7.24   A d.c. restoration circuit which restores to a positive voltage

The diode in the circuit does not conduct when the waveform is positive, but passes current when the wave swings negative relative to the zero (earth) line. When the diode conducts, capacitor C is charged positively and has a positive voltage between its plates when the diode ceases to conduct. This positive voltage is equal to the missing d.c. voltage, and the diode will thereafter conduct only as required i.e., on negative peaks to keep the voltage across the capacitor at the correct level.

A d.c. restoration circuit which ensures that the minimum voltage of a waveform is *higher than earth (zero voltage)* is shown in Figure 7.24. This raises the minimum level by V volts, the battery voltage.

Limiting means restricting the peak amplitude of a signal, preferably without clipping it to do so. It can be carried out with the aid of a voltage divider, one part of which is a controllable resistance (which is often either a transistor or a FET – Volume 2 of this series). A feature of both these types of semiconductor is that the resistance between two of their three electrodes depends on the voltage at the third electrode.

A typical limiting circuit is shown in block form in Figure 7.25. The amplitude of the waveform is used to generate a d.c. voltage (see Chapter 10). This d.c. voltage is used to control the resistance of a transistor or FET used as a

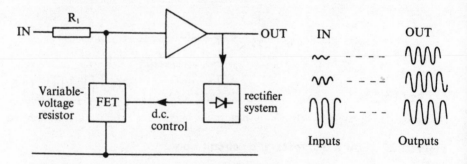

Figure 7.25   A limiting amplifer in block diagram

controllable resistor in a voltage divider. If the amplitude of the signal increases, the d.c. level increases also – and this increased d.c. voltage is used to *decrease* the resistance of the controllable resistor, so reducing the amplitude of the signal leaving the divider. The effect is that, whatever the amplitude of the input signal, the output amplitude becomes almost constant.

The circuit can be adjusted so that only signals above a pre-set voltage limit are treated in this way.

Limiting circuits of this type are widely used in tape recorders as automatic recording level controls or as overload prevention circuits, and in radio transmitters to prevent over-modulation.

The addition of time-related waveforms

It is also possible to add together the instantaneous values of two waveforms to make a third waveform, of different shape; and the concept can be extended to the addition of the instantaneous values of many waves. The principle is illustrated in Figure 7.26.

It is indeed possible to show that *any* square or triangular waveform consists of the addition to a fundamental sine wave of an infinite number of its own harmonics. The distortions produced by non-linearity in amplifiers, in particular, can be analysed in this way.

If, however, a square or triangular wave is passed through a low-pass filter, the process is reversed and the higher-order harmonics are *subtracted* from the input wave. When a 1 kHz square or triangular wave, for instance, is passed through a filter which attenuates all frequencies above 1.5 kHz, the resulting output in both cases will be a sinewave of 1 kHz frequency.

Exercise 7.2
Construct the filter circuit illustrated in Figure 7.27, using a signal generator as the signal source and an electronic voltmeter as the detector. The inductor and

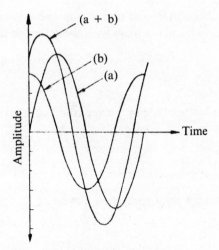

Figure 7.26   The addition of time-related waveforms

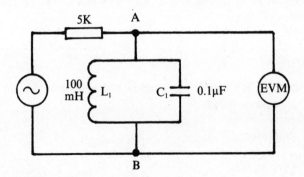

Figure 7.27   Diagram for Exercise 7.1

capacitor should have values as indicated – use a polyester type of capacitor.

Start with the signal generator set to deliver 1V output at a frequency of 1000 Hz. Read the output of the voltmeter and if the reading is too small for the lowest range of the instrument, increase the output of the signal generator until a reading can be taken. Now increase the frequency in steps of 100 Hz, taking a reading of output at each frequency up to 2000 Hz. Plot your readings on a graph of amplitude (Y-axis) against frequency.

When you have plotted the graph, find by adjusting the signal generator the frequency for which the output amplitude is a maximum, and confirm that this could also be deduced from your graph.

Now rearrange the circuit so that the inductor and the capacitor are in series between points A and B. Take readings of amplitude and frequency once again between 1000 Hz and 2000 Hz, and plot a graph of the results. How does the action of the series LC circuit compare with the action of the parallel circuit?

Test questions

7.1 The peak to peak amplitude of a wave could be measured using
(a) a digital voltmeter
(b) an oscilloscope
(c) an analogue meter
(d) a multimeter.

7.2 If a wave has a d.c. component, then it must be
(a) a sine wave
(b) a square wave
(c) a wave symmetrical about earth potential
(d) a wave asymmetrical about earth potential.

7.3 A 1 MHz wave travelling at 3×10^8 m/s has a wavelength of
(a) 3 cm
(b) 30 cm
(c) 300 cm
(d) 300 m.

7.4 The amplitude of a square wave can be reduced without seriously affecting its wave shape by using
(a) a clipper
(b) an integrator
(c) a d.c. restorer
(d) a differentiator.

7.5 A d.c. signal component cannot be passed by a
(a) capacitor
(b) resistor
(c) inductor
(d) VDR.

7.6 A 1 KHz square wave is passed through a filter circuit with a cut-off frequency of 1.5 KHz. The output wave-shape is
(a) a square wave
(b) a sawtooth
(c) a sine wave
(d) a pulse train.

8   Amplifiers and oscillators

Refer to syllabus sections 04(4. 5) and 07(005)

An amplifier which produces at its output terminals a large signal which is in all other respects, especially as regards frequency and wave-shape, an exact copy of the signal at its input terminals is termed a *linear amplifier*.

When the output signal has greater voltage amplitude than the input signal, the amplifier is said to have *voltage gain*. This gain is defined as the ratio:

$$\frac{\text{Output signal voltage}}{\text{Input signal voltage}}$$

When the output signal has greater current amplitude than the input signal, the amplifier is said to have *current gain*. This gain is defined as the ratio:

$$\frac{\text{Output signal current}}{\text{Input signal current}}$$

When an amplifier produces both voltage and current gain, its output signal will have greater power than its input signal. The *power gain* of the amplifier is defined as:

$$\frac{\text{Signal power out}}{\text{Signal power in}} = \text{Voltage gain} \times \text{current gain}$$

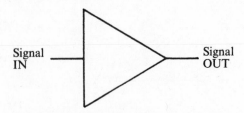

Figure 8.1   The symbol for an amplifier

An amplifier is represented on a block diagram by the arrowhead symbol shown in Figure 8.1. The output terminal is always assumed to be at the tip of the arrowhead.

Amplifiers are classified according to the range of signal frequencies which they are designed to handle. It is necessary for design principles to be modified according to the frequency range. Detailed amplifier circuits are covered in Volume 2 of this series. In this chapter, only the measurable features of amplifiers are discussed, not details of their circuitry.

Voltage, current and power gains, all defined above, are three parameters of any amplifier which can be measured. To measure the gain of an amplifier, a signal is injected into the input and the amplitude of the output signal is measured (see Figure 8.2). For most purposes, voltage gain is the figure of most interest, and it is the voltages of the input and output signals which have to be measured. Suitable input signals are obtained from a signal generator fitted with a calibrated attenuator – a circuit which reduces the signal by a given amount (e.g. $\div 10$, $\div 100$, $\div 1000$).

The output signal is generally measured against the Y (vertical deflection) amplifier calibration of a cathode-ray oscilloscope (CRO).

A problem sometimes encountered is for the input signal from the signal generator to be too small to be measured by the oscilloscope. In practical work, for example, a signal as low as 30m Vp-p could often be usefully measured; but few of the oscilloscopes used in servicing can reliably measure such a quantity. To overcome the difficulty, the attenuator is switched so that the signal is made ten times greater at 300mV, or even one hundred times greater at 3V. Quantities such as these can be readily measured with the CRO; and when this has been done, the attenuator is reset to reduce the signal generator output to the value corresponding to a 30mV input.

The same technique can be used to set any other value of signal generator voltage that may be required.

When both input and output signals have been measured, the voltage gain is found by use of the formula:

$$G = \frac{\text{Output voltage signal}}{\text{Input voltage signal}}$$

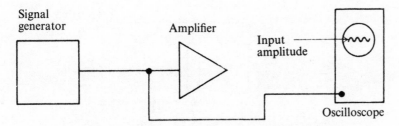

(a) Oscilloscope measures amplitude of INPUT SIGNAL

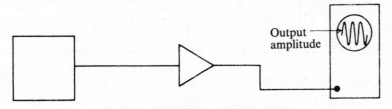

(b) Oscilloscope measures amplitude of OUTPUT SIGNAL

(c) Voltage gain (G) = $\dfrac{\text{Output amplitude}}{\text{Input amplitude}}$

Figure 8.2   Measuring voltage gain

Exercise 8.1
Construct the voltage amplifier shown in Figure 8.3, using a BC107 or BFY50 transistor. Connect the amplifier to a 9V supply and check that the collector voltage falls within the range 4V to 5V. Use the oscilloscope to set the sine-wave of the signal generator to 30mV p-p at 400 Hz.

Connect the output of the signal generator to the input of the amplifier, and the output of the amplifier to the oscilloscope. Measure the peak-to-peak amplitude of the signal from the output of the amplifier.

Then calculate the voltage gain from the formula:

$$G = \frac{\text{Output voltage p-p}}{\text{Input voltage p-p}}$$

Similar methods are used to measure the *bandwidth* of an amplifier. This is the range of frequencies over which the amplifier can be effectively used. The upper and lower limits of bandwidth are taken to be the frequencies at which the voltage gain of the amplifier is *70.7 per cent only* of its value in the middle of the frequency range.

The bandwidth of an amplifier is expressed in one of two ways: by quoting either the two limiting frequencies or the difference between them. Thus the

133

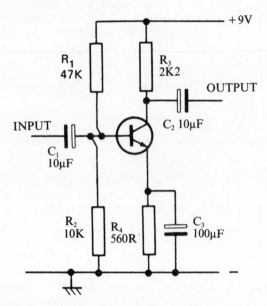

Figure 8.3   Diagram for Exercise 8.1

bandwidth of an audio amplifier may be quoted as, for example, '40 Hz to 25 kHz', or the bandwidth of a radio-frequency amplifier as '10 kHz centred on 465 kHz'. Specifically, the bandwidth is defined as the frequency range between the two -3dB or half-power points.

Bandwidth is assessed by plotting the actual voltage gain of the amplifier at a range of different frequencies. A graph of gain plotted against frequency (Figure 8.4) then shows the two frequencies at which the gain has fallen to '$1/\sqrt{2}$, which corresponds to 70.7 per cent of midband gain'.

Note that the X axis of the graph along which frequency is measured is calibrated on a *logarithmic* scale in order to accommodate the wide range of frequencies covered by a typical amplifier bandwidth.

Exercise 8.2

In the circuit shown in Figure 8.5, measure voltage gain at 50 Hz, 100 Hz, 200 Hz, 1 kHz, 2 kHz, 4 kHz, 8 kHz, 12 kHz and 20 kHz. On logarithmic graph paper (linear by 4-cycle log) plot a graph of voltage gain against frequency for the amplifier in question (which you will find has purposely been given component values which will give it a narrow bandwidth). From this deduce the bandwidth.

In every amplifier, the quantities of *input resistance* and *output resistance* can be measured. The input resistance of an amplifier is given by the ratio:

$$\frac{\text{Signal voltage}}{\text{Signal current}} \text{ at the input terminals.}$$

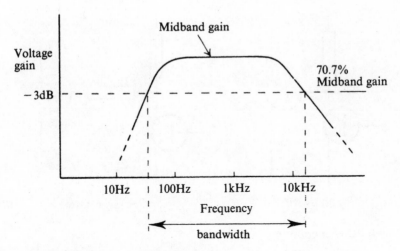

Figure 8.4   A graph of bandwidth

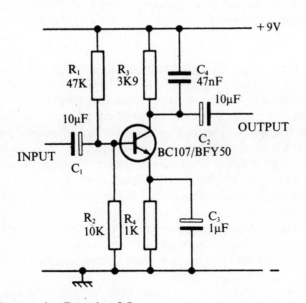

Figure 8.5   Diagram for Exercise 8.2

An amplifier with low input resistance will require more signal current at the input than will a similar amplifier with large input resistance. A large loss of signal will occur if an amplifier with low input resistance is driven from a signal source having a high output resistance.

Note that, when the amplifier is being used to amplify high-frequency signals,

135

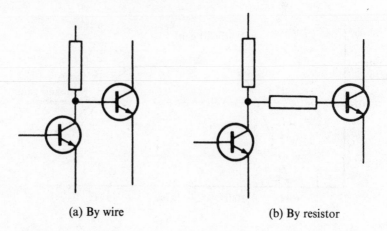

(a) By wire   (b) By resistor

Figure 8.6   Direct coupling

the quantities 'input resistance' and 'output resistance' are more usually, and more correctly, referred to as *input and output impedances*.

The output resistance of an amplifier is given by the ratio:

$$\frac{\text{Signal voltage at output}}{\text{Signal current at output}}.$$

If the amplifier is to be used to drive a low-resistance load such as a loudspeaker or a motor, the value of output resistance must be low – no more than a few ohms. Most voltage amplifiers, however, have higher values of output resistance than that – a typical value being a few kilohms.

When a single stage of amplification does not provide enough gain, several amplifier stages are coupled together in series or in cascade. *Coupling* means passing signal voltages from the output of one amplifier stage and using them as the input of the next.

Stages may be coupled in several ways. If the coupling is by means of a wire or a resistor – Figure 8.6 – the coupling is said to be *direct*. The other principal methods of coupling are *capacitor coupling* and *transformer coupling* (Figure 8.7).

With direct coupling, the d.c. voltage at the output of the first stage becomes the d.c. voltage at the input of the second stage. When capacitor or transformer coupling is employed, the two voltages in question can be quite different.

Whatever the method of coupling, the input resistance of a stage is always *in parallel* with the signal itself, and the output resistance *in series* with it. Thus the output resistance of one stage always forms a potential divider with the input resistance of the next stage (see Figure 8.8 and R_o and R_i in Figure 8.9).

Any potential divider is bound by its very nature to reduce signal voltage –

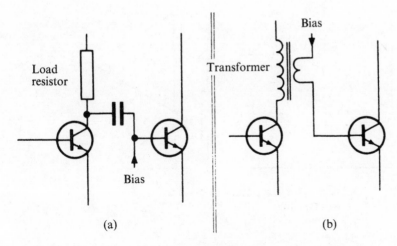

Figure 8.7 Capacitor coupling (a) and transformer coupling (b)

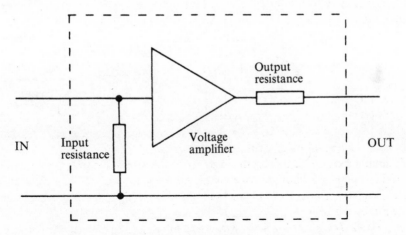

Figure 8.8 Input resistance is in parallel with signal output resistance in series with signal

with the result that the joint voltage gain of any two consecutive stages (which might have been expected to be the product of the individual stage gain) is in practice always less than the value which this straight calculation would give.

As already stated, the function of a linear amplifier is to generate an exact but enlarged copy of a waveform. If the wave-shape at the output of the amplifier is not a true copy of the wave-shape at the input, the amplifier is said to be producing *distortion*. Distortion can be caused by overloading – i.e. by putting in a signal input whose peak-to-peak voltage is greater than the amplifier can

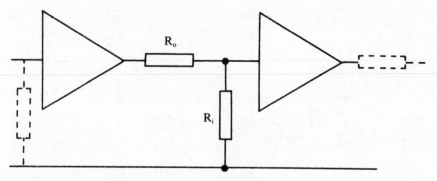

Figure 8.9 R_o and R_i form a potential divider

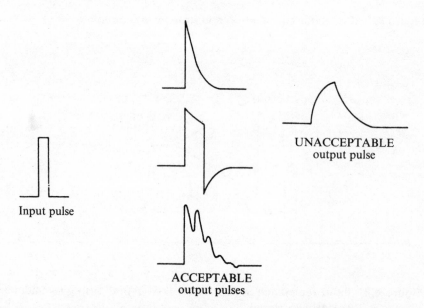

Figure 8.10 Pulse amplifiers: acceptable and unacceptable output wave-forms

accept. If signal input is normal, distortion generally indicates a fault in the amplifier circuit itself.

Not all amplifiers are linear, however. *Pulse amplifiers*, for example, are not intended to preserve in every respect the shape of the wave they amplify. The one thing a pulse amplifier must not do is *alter the slope of the leading edges* of the pulse inputs (see Figure 8.10).

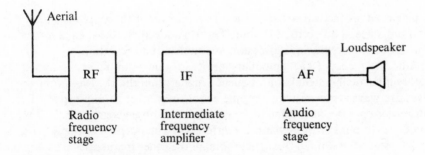

Figure 8.11   Simplified diagram of a radio receiver

Classes of amplifier circuit

Audio frequency (AF) amplifiers handle the range of frequencies lying within the approximate range 30 Hz to 20 kHz. This is about the range of frequencies which can be detected by the (younger) human ear. Such amplifiers are used in record players and tape recording, in the sound section of TV receivers, in cinema sound circuits and in many industrial applications.

Frequencies up to about 100 kHz, though well beyond the range of the human ear, are often for convenience included in the AF range of a signal generator.

AF voltage amplifiers have fairly high voltage gain, and medium-to-high values of output resistance. AF power amplifiers give large values of current gain. They have very low output resistance so can pass large signal currents into low-resistance loads such as loudspeakers.

Fault conditions are indicated by low gain (or no gain at all), by waveform distortion, by reduced bandwidth, or by changes in the input or output resistances.

Intermediate frequency (IF) amplifiers are used in radio receivers of all kinds (sound, TV, radar, etc.). The 'intermediate frequency' is so called because it lies between the radio frequencies which are picked up by the aerial and the much lower frequencies which are finally fed to the loudspeaker or cathode ray tube. Typical intermediate frequencies are 470kHz for AM radios, 10.7 MKz for FM radios, 33.5 to 39.5 MHz for TV and 50 MHz upwards for radar.

The bandwidth of an IF amplifier can be either small – 10 kHz for an AM radio – or large, such as the 5.5 MHz bandwidth of the IF in a TV receiver – or very large, such as the 10 MHz or higher for the IF of a radar set.

An IF amplifier is usually a *tuned* amplifier, which means that its gain is greatest at one particular frequency. This high-gain frequency can be varied by adjusting the values of components (usually inductors and capacitors) within the amplifier itself.

Distortion is not generally a problem in IF amplifiers, because the tuning circuit preserves the wave-shape of a sine-wave even if the amplifier itself does not. Faults which do occur in IF amplifiers (in addition to those encountered in all linear amplifiers) include low gain, mis-tuning and oscillation.

Radio frequency (RF) amplifiers are also tuned amplifiers designed to amplify a particular signal at a frequency higher than the IF. Radio-frequency waves are waves transmitted from one aerial to another through space. Every transmitter operates at a different frequency from those geographically close to it, in order to minimize co-channel interference. The purpose of the RF amplifier is to select the wanted frequency from all the other frequencies reaching the aerial (an operation called tuning), and then to amplify this frequency. The purpose of this immediate RF amplification is to make the amplitude of the peak-to-peak voltage of the desired signal larger than that of all other signals picked up by the aerial – including the so-called noise signals, which are unwanted signals derived from sources which are not transmitters in the normal sense.

RF amplifiers may have a fairly wide bandwidth and low input resistance. Although voltage gain may be low, there is usually a significant current gain. RF amplifiers for operation beyond about 50 GHz are very difficult to construct, and should be returned to the manufacturer if found to be faulty.

Amplitude-modulated (AM) radios do not normally possess RF stages unless high gain and selectivity (the ability to select a wanted station without interference from others) is required. Such stages, however, are found in car radios. VHF radios and TV receivers make use of RF stages as *buffers* (see below) to prevent signals generated inside the receiver from being fed back to the aerial.

Typical RF amplifier faults include mistuning and oscillation, in addition to the usual range of linear amplifier faults.

D.c. amplifiers, as their name suggests, are used to amplify d.c. voltages or very low-frequency signals. A d.c. amplifier with a gain of 100, for example, could produce an output of 1 V d.c. from an input of 10 millivolts d.c.

D.c. amplifiers are used in industrial electronic circuits such as photocell counters, in measuring instruments such as strain gauges, and in medical electronics (where they could be used to measure, for example, the electrical voltages in human muscles).

The main problem with d.c. amplifiers is their *stability*. It is difficult to ensure that their d.c. output does not vary, or *drift*, from one minute to the next, or charge as room temperature changes. Voltage drift is thus the main fault of d.c. amplifiers, but variations in gain and a type of instability which causes either low-frequency or high-frequency oscillations are also sources of operating trouble.

Feedback amplifiers. In a practical situation, it is sometimes necessary to modify the characteristics of a basic amplifier circuit. Such modifications involve the application of feedback from amplifier output to input and the exact effect depends upon whether the feedback signal aids or opposes the original

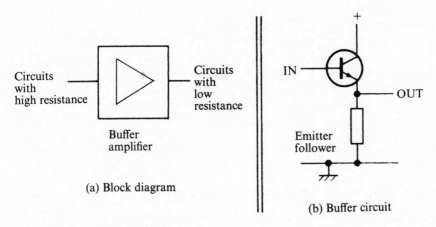

(a) Block diagram

(b) Buffer circuit

Figure 8.12   The buffer amplifier

input. If the signals are aiding, the technique is described as positive feedback and this leads to increased gain with reduced bandwidth. However if this feedback is increased, a point will be reached when the amplifier becomes an oscillator. Conversely, when the two signals are in anti-phase, the feedback is described as negative. This leads to a reduction in gain but with an increased bandwidth.

Wide-band amplifiers are amplifiers which provide the same value of gain over a large range of frequencies – typically from d.c. to several MHz. One important special application is as signal amplifiers in oscilloscopes; but it is true to say that most equipment used to make measurements on signal voltages will include a wide-band amplifier.

No form of tuning is possible for such amplifiers; and their design is complicated by the requirement that they must provide the same values of voltage gain for d.c. as they do for high-frequency a.c. signals. Common faults include instability of bandwidth, variations in gain, and the danger of oscillation.

Buffer amplifiers are inserted into a system to prevent one stage from producing unstabilizing feedback effects on adjacent stages. The device used is commonly the emitter follower circuit of Figure 8.12 which has very high and very low input and output resistances respectively to provide a good impedance match between stages. Although the circuit produces only unity voltage gain, it provides a significant current gain. A similar circuit using a field effect transistor is known as a *source follower*.

Video amplifiers are a species of wide-band amplifier used for the specific purpose of amplifying signals to be applied to cathode ray tubes (CRTs). The video signal is the signal which carries all picture information for TV or radar sets, and the video amplifier is the circuit used for amplifying it. A frequency range from d.c. to 5.5 MHz is desirable in video amplifiers used in TV, but a still

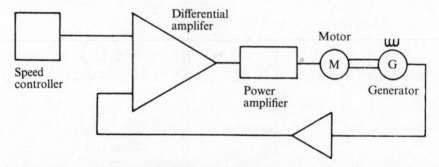

Figure 8.13   How a differential amplifier is used

wider range is required to handle most radar signals.

Differential amplifiers, unlike the types mentioned so far, have two inputs, with their output signal an amplified version of the *difference* between the signals at the inputs. Such amplifiers are much used when it is desired to compare two signals with a view to making the difference between them as small as possible.

The speed controller system shown in Figure 8.13 is an example of how a differential amplifier is used. One signal (which can be either a.c. or d.c.) is applied to the differential amplifier from the speed controller. The other signal comes from a small generator (a *tachogenerator*) coupled to the motor. The output of the differential amplifier is further amplified by either a d.c. or an a.f. power amplifier, and then used to drive the motor.

Any change in the speed of the motor will cause a change in the output of the tachogenerator. This change, in turn, will cause a difference to arise between the two inputs to the differential amplifier. This difference is amplified and used to speed up or slow down the motor, as required, until normal speed is restored.

Oscillators

An oscillator is an amplifier that provides its own input using positive feedback. That is, a signal is derived from the output and fed back into the input in phase so as to sustain the output signal. The feedback network usually consists of frequency determining components such as shown in Figure 8.14. There are two conditions that have to be met to sustain oscillations, the amplifier gain must be greater than the attenuation of the feedback loop and the feedback must be positive. If the loop gain is only marginally greater than 1, then the output wave-shape will be sinusoidal. If however, the gain is much greater than 1, oscillations will be rather violent and this results in pulse or square wave-shapes. The frequency of oscillations depends upon the values of the components in the feedback loop and the output amplitude depends largely on circuit component

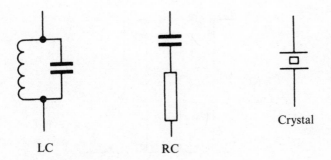

LC   RC   Crystal

Figure 8.14 Networks used in sine-wave oscillators

and supply voltage values. The essential function of an oscillator is to convert the d.c. power supplied into it into a.c. power as the output signal and like all energy converting devices, it dissipates heat due to its inefficiencies.

LC networks consist, as the name implies, of inductors and capacitors. The frequency of oscillation is directly related to the values of inductance and capacitance used.

$$f_o = \frac{1}{2\pi\sqrt{LC}} \text{ Hz}$$

Where f_o = frequency of oscillator, L = inductance in Henries, C = capacitance in Farads. LC oscillators provide a good sine-wave shape and have reasonable *frequency stability*. This latter phrase means that the frequency does not alter extensively when either the supply voltage or the temperature alters. LC oscillators are used for generating radio frequencies in applications where accurate frequency stability is not of prime importance.

CR oscillators are used to generate sine-wave signals at audio frequencies (below about 100kHz) in applications for which LC oscillators are unsuitable because of the very large size of inductor which would be required. CR (or RC – both terms are used) oscillators consist of passive networks containing capacitors and resistors, so they need additional circuits to control the amplitude of oscillation. Without such additional circuitry, the output waveform of a CR oscillator would always be of poor shape.

Crystal oscillators are used to generate radio frequencies, and the higher ranges of audio frequencies, in applications where the greatest possible degree of frequency stability is required. The network which determines the frequency and wave-shape is a vibrating quartz crystal whose vibrations are sustained by electrical power from an amplifier circuit. Crystal oscillators are used in time-keeping circuits such as clocks and watches, and in radio transmitters.

Pulse (or *astable* or *aperiodic*) oscillators also contain a network which acts as a time control, plus an amplifier. The amplifier is, as is usual in oscillator

143

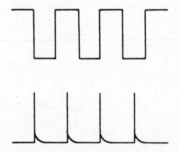

Figure 8.15   The pulse or aperiodic oscillator: output waveforms

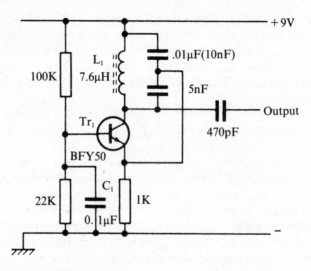

Figure 8.16   The Colpitts oscillator

circuits, so connected that its input is provided from its own output signal by positive feedback; but the operating principle on which it works is different from that of a sinusoidal oscillator.

In all pulse oscillators, the amplifier is in operation for only a very short time in any cycle – often for less than a microsecond. For the remainder of the cycle, the waveform is generated by the changing level of the voltage across a capacitor as a resistor feeds current into the capacitor or drains current out of it. It is only the steeply sloping sides of the waveform which are caused by amplifier action. All the remaining parts of the waveform are generated by the resistor–capacitor network.

Exercise 8.3

Construct the oscillator circuits shown in Figures 8.16 and 8.17. The circuit of Figure 8.16 is a sine-wave oscillator of a type called a *Colpitts oscillator*. It

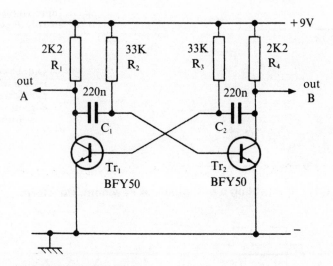

Figure 8.17   A multivibrator circuit

generates a sine-wave at a frequency of around 1 MHz. The coil L1 consists of 25 turns of wire occupying a width of 11mm on a former 7mm in diameter, with a ferrite core.

When the circuit has been built and checked, connect the output to the oscilloscope and connect a 9V supply to the oscillator. Measure the amplitude and frequency of the output. Now connect the second circuit, and again measure the amplitude and frequency of the output, and sketch the waveform.

The circuit of Figure 8.17 is a square-wave oscillator of a type called a *multivibrator*. Do not dismantle the multivibrator when you have finished experimenting with it, but retain it for use in a later Exercise.

Sawtooth oscillators work on the same principles as do pulse oscillators save that they make use of the change of voltage across a capacitor or of the change of current flow through an inductor. When a voltage is applied to a capacitor across a resistor, as in Figure 8.18, the capacitor cannot charge immediately, but does so in the form of a curve called an *exponential* rise. A small section of the first part of this waveform is almost straight (because an uncharged capacitor accepts an initial charge very readily). Therefore if the amplifier discharges the capacitor before it has had time to charge to more than a small fraction of the applied voltage, a waveform of sawtooth shape will be produced. Such a wave-shape is often termed a *serrasoid*.

The action is equivalent to that of an integrator fed with a square wave. Several sawtooth oscillator circuits, indeed, consist of square-wave generators coupled to integrating circuits (see Figure 8.19).

An oscillator, operating correctly, should provide an output signal whenever a d.c. supply is connected to it. A faulty oscillator may be revealed by failure to

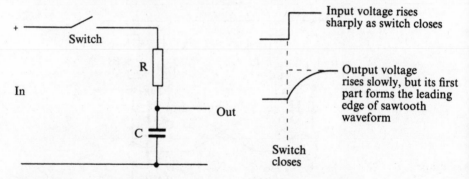

Figure 8.18   Generating a triangular, or sawtooth, waveform

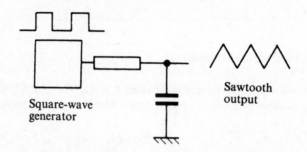

Figure 8.19   Square-wave generator with sawtooth output

produce an output signal (or at best an intermittent one) or by generating an output waveform of distorted wave-shape, incorrect frequency or insufficient amplitude.

The phase-locked loop

A network much used to maintain a *constant output frequency* from a voltage–controlled oscillator (VCO) is the *phase-locked loop* (or *PLL*). A block diagram is shown in Figure 8.20.

The PLL works by feeding a proportion of the output signal back to the phase discriminator, where it is compared with another frequency (which may be a reference signal). Any discrepancy between the two generates an *error signal*, which is then amplified and applied to the VCO where it corrects for any previous frequency drift.

The phase discriminator is thus the heart of the PLL, for it is there that the instantaneous values of input signal and of the signal derived by feedback from the output are multiplied together. The usual rules of arithmetic apply (*plus*

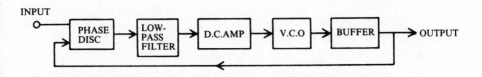

Figure 8.20   The phase-locked loop: block diagram

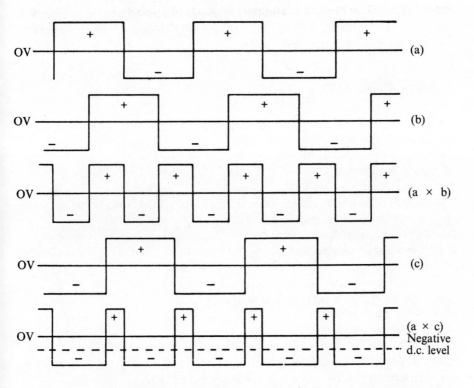

Figure 8.21   The phase discriminator in the PLL system: input and output waveforms

times *plus* = +, *minus* times *plus* = −, *minus* times *minus* = +), so that the output becomes a new waveform. This is shown in Figure 8.21 (where square waves are shown for simplicity though the result would have been similar had the more usual sine waves been shown instead).

If the two signals being compared have the same frequency but differ in time

147

by a quarter of a period, the resultant will be a second harmonic with a d.c. component of zero (a × b in Figure 8.21). If this phase relationship changes, however, the output of the phase discrimination will develop either a positive or a negative d.c. component depending on the direction of the phase change (a × c in Figure 8.21).

The *low pass filter* (see Figure 8.20) removes the a.c. component, so that the d.c. level can be *amplified*. When this amplified signal is applied to the VCO, it so corrects the frequency of the latter that it is made to agree with, or *follow*, the frequency of the reference signal.

The system can thus be used, e.g., to provide a constant-speed output from an a.c. motor. Alternatively, if the input to the phase discriminator is an FM signal, the VCO is made to follow the frequency variations of this signal, which represents of course the modulation component. The error signal itself then becomes the demodulated audio signal.

Test Questions

8.1   An audio amplifier is NOT suitable for use as a video amplifier because its
(a) bandwidth is too narrow
(b) frequency response is too flat
(c) gain is insufficient
(d) output signal contains no d.c. component.
8.2   The bandwidth of an amplifier is measured approximately between the frequencies at which the response is
(a) 10 per cent of peak value
(b) 30 per cent of peak value
(c) 50 per cent of peak value
(d) 70 per cent of peak value.
8.3   A pulse amplifier is faulty if it distorts
(a) the amplitude of a pulse
(b) the width of a pulse
(c) the leading edge of a pulse
(d) the trailing edge of a pulse.
8.4   An oscillator must contain a frequency-determining network plus
(a) an amplifier with positive feedback
(b) an amplifier with negative feedback
(c) a perfectly linear amplifier
(d) a distorting amplifier.
8.5   The bandwidth of a typical video amplifier extends from
(a) 20 Hz to 20kHz
(b) 470 kHz to 10.7 MHz
(c) d.c. to 5.5 MHz

(d) d.c. to 4.43 MHz.

8.6 A multivibrator output is fed into an integrator circuit. This results in an output that is

(a) a square wave

(b) a sine wave

(c) a sawtooth wave

(d) a sine wave with a d.c. component.

9 Radio transmission and reception

Refer to syllabus sections 04(4.5) and 07(005)

One of the earliest applications of electronics was in the transmission and reception of radio waves.

Any a.c. signal is radiated into the air from a wire. Waves of very low frequency, such as the 50 Hz used for power supplies, would radiate effectively only if the wire carrying them were extremely long (in the region of several million metres); but waves of higher 'radio' frequency, which means above 100 kHz, radiate more easily.

It was discovered early in the history of radio that if the radiating wire, called an *aerial* or *antenna*, were cut to a length exactly one-quarter of the wavelength of the signal, it would radiate very efficiently. Such a quarter-wavelength aerial behaves to a signal wave as if it were a special kind of resistor – one which dissipates the energy of the signal as radio waves rather than as heat (see Figure 9.1).

Aerials are also used to *receive* radio waves, converting the waves travelling through the air into signals of voltage or current in a wire leading from the aerial. Again, the exact length of the receiving aerial is critical; but in any case only a tiny fraction of the power radiated by a transmitter is ever picked up by the aerial of an individual receiver.

A transmitted signal which consists wholly of a steady radio frequency is called a *continuous wave* (CW) transmissions. Such a transmission is useless save as a means of establishing that a transmitter is indeed operating. To convey a

150

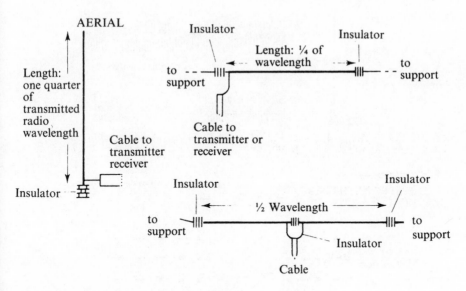

Figure 9.1 Aerials: vertical and horizonal polarization

signal, some means of varying the wave must be found.

The oldest known method is to switch the wave on and off in a pattern of longer 'dashes' and short 'dots' called the *Morse code*. A carrier interrupted in this way – whether by Morse or by any other of the many different types of telegraph code – is called an *interrupted continuous wave* (ICW) transmission (see Figure 9.2).

Though Morse was extensively used in the early days of radio for emergency transmissions and by radio amateurs, it is a relatively slow method of communication since every letter of the message has to be coded and transmitted individually. Since the early 1920s, therefore, radio communication has concentrated on varying either the amplitude or the frequency of the carrier wave itself in such a way as to transmit audio and other signals of lower frequency. Such a process is called *modulation* – the carrier wave is 'modulated' by the imposition on it of the original baseband signal.

High-frequency signals of this nature can carry many different kinds of information – whether it be audio signals at sound frequency, video signals from a TV camera, or other waveforms for such purposes as conveying digital signals from computer to computer, the transmission of facsimile copies of documents, or radar. The principal of operation is shown in Figure 9.3.

Such waveforms are derived from *transducers* – devices which convert one form of energy into another. The transducers which are of interest in electronics are those which use or provide electrical signals. One such is a *microphone*, which converts the pressure waves called sound into electrical waves of the same

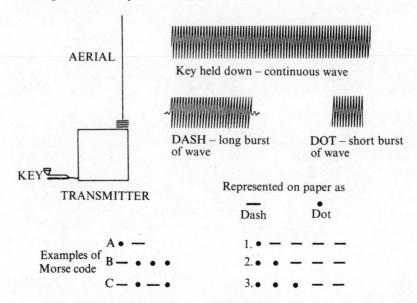

Figure 9.2   CW transmission – the Morse code

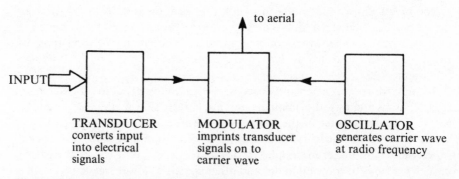

Figure 9.3   How a transmitter functions

frequency as the sound, and so forms an audio signal. The amplitude of this audio signal is proportional to the volume of the sound signal itself.

Light rays can also be converted into a signal by means of a transducer called a *photocell*; but the transmission of a light pattern or picture requires a much more complicated transducer – the *television camera-tube*. The scanning action of the TV camera tube will be briefly described in Chapter 14.

The job of the transducer at the other end of a radio system is to convert an electrical signal back to the type of signal which it originally was (see Figure 9.4). For sound signals, this transducer is the *loudspeaker*; for TV signals it is a

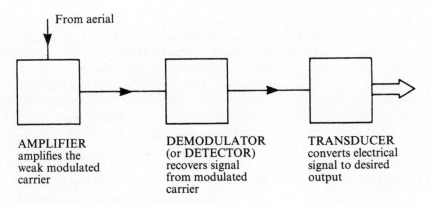

AMPLIFIER
amplifies the
weak modulated
carrier

DEMODULATOR
(or DETECTOR)
recovers signal
from modulated
carrier

TRANSDUCER
converts electrical
signal to desired
output

Figure 9.4   How a receiver functions

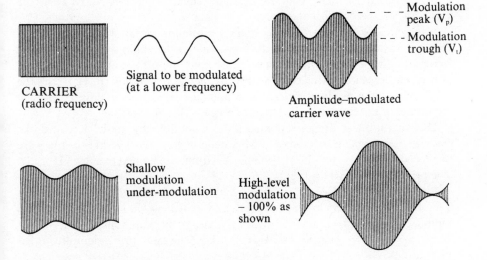

CARRIER
(radio frequency)

Signal to be modulated
(at a lower frequency)

Modulation
peak (V_p)

Modulation
trough (V_t)

Amplitude–modulated
carrier wave

Shallow
modulation
under-modulation

High-level
modulation
– 100% as
shown

Figure 9.5   The amplitude-modulated carrier

cathode-ray tube (CRT). The aerials of both transmitter and receiver are also transducers, either converting electrical signals carried on a wire into electromagnetic waves, or vice versa.

Modulation

The process called modulation alters a carrier wave of radio frequency in such a way that it 'carries' a wave of lower frequency containing a signal. One method of carrying such an audio or video signal is called *amplitude modulation* (AM) – see Figure 9.5.

153

An amplitude modulator is a circuit into which two signals are fed – the carrier wave at a high (radio) frequency and the modulating signal at a lower (audio or video) frequency. The output of the modulator is a signal at carrier frequency whose amplitude exactly follows the amplitude changes of the modulating signal. The greater the amplitude of the modulating signal, the greater the depth of modulation of the carrier. Excessive amplitude of the modulating signal causes over-modulation of the carrier itself, resulting in distortion when the signal is recovered by demodulation.

Exercise 9.1
From the oscillator circuit built for Exercise 8.3 remove C1. Connect the low-resistance output terminals of an audio signal generator to the base of the transistor, and to earth – making the connection to the base of the transistor through a 1µF capacitor. Connect the oscilloscope to the output of the oscillator, switch on the supply (but not the audio signal generator), and observe the sine-wave on the oscilloscope screen.

Now set the signal generator to 400Hz, minimum amplitude, and switch on. Observe the modulated signal as the amplitude of the audio signal is increased. Sketch the shape of the trace at several different amplitudes of modulation.

A second type of modulation is called *frequency modulation* (FM). It uses the amplitude of the modulating signal to alter the *frequency* of the carrier. The amplitude of the carrier itself remains constant throughout.

The alteration of frequency caused by a modulating signal is called the *frequency deviation*. In wide-band FM systems deviations of 75 kHz or more are produced; in narrow-band FM systems deviations are limited to a few kHz only. The principle is shown in Figure 9.6.

Another system called *pulse modulation* operates by switching the carrier on and off in a pattern resembling Morse code, but at a very much faster rate. Pulse modulation is used mainly for radar signals, or in communications systems using carriers at frequencies above 1000 MHz. The basic principle is illustrated in Figure 9.7.

A pulse signal can be modulated for communications purposes in several different ways. *Pulse amplitude modulation* (PAM) systems modulate the amplitude of the pulses in the same way as the amplitude of a continuous carrier is modulated in the AM system. Note, however, that each pulse consists of a large number of cycles of a carrier at a very high frequency, and that the *pulse repetition rate* (p.r.r.) needs to be greater than the modulating frequency.

Pulse width modulation (PWM) systems use the modulating signal to change the width of the pulse of carrier waves. A sine-wave modulation, for example, appears as illustrated in Figure 9.8, where the widest pulse of the modulated carrier corresponds to the positive peak of the signal and the narrowest pulse to the negative peak.

Pulse position modulation (PPM) leaves both the amplitude and the width of

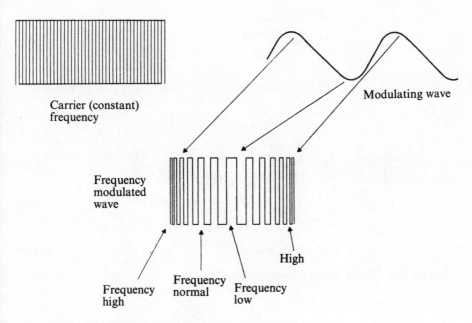

Carrier (constant) frequency

Modulating wave

Frequency modulated wave

High

Frequency high

Frequency normal

Frequency low

Figure 9.6   The principle of frequency modulation

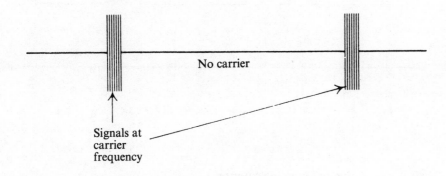

No carrier

Signals at carrier frequency

Figure 9.7   The principle of pulse modulation

the pulses unchanged, but alters the time intervals at which they occur. A pulse repeated at regular intervals carries zero modulation, but if the timing of a pulse is varied so that it occurs either before or after the 'normal' time of its recurrence, this variation from its set time is used to carry information of the amplitude of a signal. When the arrival of a pulse is delayed *after* its set time, it indicates *positive* peak of signal. When it arrives *before* its set time, it indicates *negative* peak of signal. The system is illustrated in Figure 9.9, in which arrows indicate the set, or 'normal', times of arrival of the pulses.

155

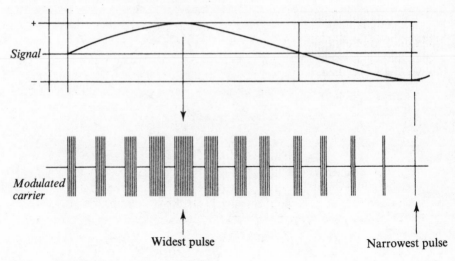

Figure 9.8 Pulse width modulation

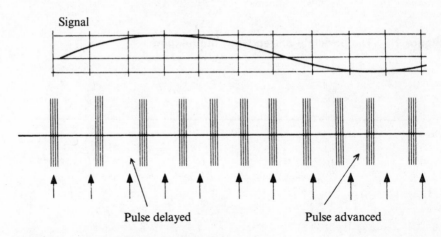

Figure 9.9 Pulse position modulation

Pulse code modulation is a very popular technique for modern communications which converts the analogue signal to be transmitted into a digital format by the process of *sampling* or measuring the amplitude at precise intervals of time. The amplitude of each sample is then converted into a binary code and this is then transmitted by one of the forms of pulse modulation. Because PCM and PPM systems handle constant amplitude and width pulses, both are relatively immune to interference problems.

Multiplex operations. The electromagnetic spectrum is not an infinite resource so that its use becomes subject to environmental considerations. Various techniques can be used to maximize spectrum availability and multiplex operations are a way of achieving this. A signal multiplex concept implies that two or more communications channels are using the same medium simultaneously. The whole spectrum forms a *frequency multiplex* as it is divided up into channels of various bandwidths, each being allocated to a particular carrier for a specific service. A further development known as a *time multiplex* allows the same carrier frequency to be used many times over by allocating that carrier to a specific channel for brief periods of time in a cyclic manner. Signals for any specific transmitter are thus interleaved with information from other transmitters. The same carrier can be used at least twice for analogue modulation, by allocating differently phased versions of it to different baseband signals. Digital and pulse modulation systems adapt very easily to some very clever multiplex operations to save bandwidth. However, all these systems require very careful synchronization at the receiver in order to recover the original modulating signals.

The Modulated signal

The simplest unmodulated carrier consists of a sine-wave having a single value of frequency. Whenever such a carrier is changed *in any way*, however, other frequencies can be detected in it. These frequencies caused by modulation are called *sidebands*. Any serviceable receiver must be able to receive these side-bands as well as the carrier wave itself.

An amplitude-modulated (AM) carrier has the simplest sideband structure. Imagine a carrier at 400 kHz modulated by an audio signal which is a 2 kHz sine-wave. The effect of modulation is to produce two new sideband frequencies – one at 402 kHz (carrier *plus* modulation frequency) and the other at 398 kHz (carrier *minus* modulation frequency), in addition to the carrier frequency of 400 kHz itself. When the modulation is at its maximum, the amplitude of each sideband should be exactly half the amplitude of the unmodulated carrier. The effect is illustrated (in exaggerated form) in Figure 9.10.

Over-modulation occurs when the modulating signal has a peak-to-peak amplitude greater than half the p.-p. amplitude of the carrier (see Figure 9.11). Such over-modulation causes severe distortion of the waveform of the modulating signal and is one of the reasons why AM is no longer used to transmit high-quality sound signals. At the transmitter, over-modulation is prevented by means of *limiting circuits* which reduce the extent of the distortion.

Under-modulation causes no distortion, but it makes the received audio signal very faint and therefore easily drowned out by electrical noise and interference signals. Persistent over-or under-modulation is a clear sign of a faulty modulator system.

When a carrier is modulated by an audio signal derived from speech or music,

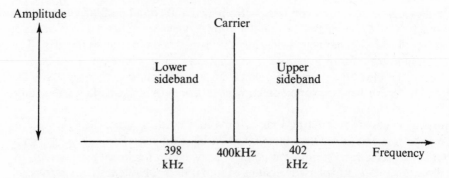

Figure 9.10   Sidebands of a carrier modulated by a sine-wave

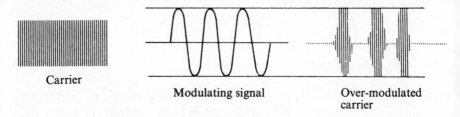

Figure 9.11   Over-modulation

the audio signal that results is not a single sine-wave, but a mixture of frequencies. The range of frequencies present in the modulation is called the *bandwidth* of the modulation or the baseband signal. Speech can be satisfactorily transmitted over a bandwidth of a mere 3 kHz, but music requires bandwidths up to 20 kHz for high-quality signals to be satisfactorily received and reproduced.

A carrier which has been amplitude-modulated by audio or video signals therefore contains sidebands which themselves consist of a mixture of frequencies and extend from $f_c - f_m$ to $f_c + f_m$, where f_c is the carrier frequency and f_m is the highest modulating frequency.

The upper sideband contains all the frequencies between f_c and $f_c + f_m$, whilst the lower sideband contains all the frequencies from $f_c - f_m$ to f_c. Given, for example, a carrier frequency of 850 kHz and modulation frequencies extending to 4 kHz on either side of it, the upper sideband would contain all the frequencies from 850 kHz to 854 kHz, and the lower sideband all the frequencies from 850 kHz to 846 kHz. Figure 9.12 shows this sideband structure which should normally be a mirror image about f_c(850 kHz).

A graph which plots the amplitude of signals against a scale of frequency is called a *spectrum*, and an instrument which displays such a graph for any signal is called a *spectrum analyser*. Figure 9.13 shows the trace of a typical AM signal displayed on such a spectrum analyser.

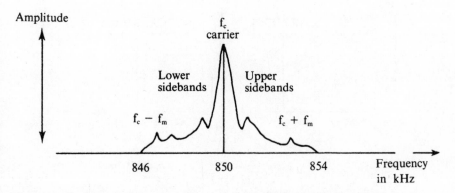

Figure 9.12   Sidebands of a carrier modulated by an audio wave

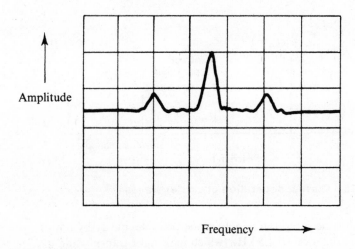

Figure 9.13   A typical spectrum analyser display

When two transmitters situated in the same geographical area start broadcasting on the same frequency, it will be impossible to receive either transmission clearly because of interference from the other. Even if their broadcasts are on different frequencies, interference will also be caused if the sidebands of the two modulated signals overlap (see Figure 9.14). It is therefore necessary that the carrier frequencies must be separated by about twice the maximum frequency of the modulating signals (see Figure 9.15) if interference is to be avoided. However, in the interests of good spectrum management, it is important to operate with the minimum channel separation.

Unfortunately, in many parts of the developed world, including Western Europe, there are many transmitters operating on the medium-wave frequen-

159

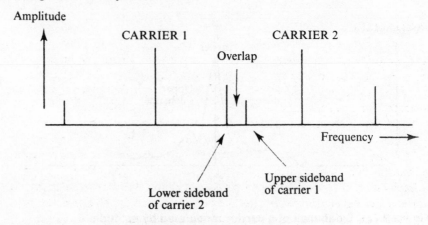

Figure 9.14   The sidebands overlap – interference

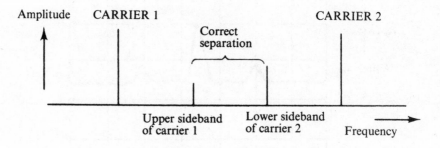

Figure 9.15   Correct separation of carrier waves

cies. Reasonable reception is only made possible, partly by limiting the bandwidth of modulation to 4.5 kHz (which makes the transmission of high-quality sound impossible), and partly by international agreement on the frequency and power output of individual transmitters.

Frequency-modulated (FM) signals have a much wider spectrum. Those radiated in the UK have an audio bandwidth of 15 kHz, with the modulated bandwidth for each sideband as wide as 200 kHz. The bandwidth of a frequency-modulated signal cannot be calculated so easily as that of an amplitude-modulated signal. It is always much the wider of the two.

Pulse modulation requires a greater bandwidth than do either AM or FM, and it cannot be used at frequencies on which too many transmitters are radiating at the same time. The bandwidths required are so great that carriers of very high frequency, of the order of 1000 MHz or more, have to be used. At such frequencies as these, pulse modulation is often the only form of modulation which can be applied by the devices which generate the carrier waves.

Demodulators

At the receiver, a demodulator is used to extract the desired modulating signal from the modulated carrier. Whether it is of audio or video frequency, the recovered signal must be free of any trace of the carrier. A low-pass filter therefore generally forms an essential part of the demodulator.

Moreover, because circuits containing diodes play a large part in demodulation, it is often possible to obtain a steady d.c. voltage, proportional in amplitude to the average amplitude of the carrier, which can be used to control the gain of the early stages of the receiver (see later in this chapter)

Each different type of modulation system requires its own peculiar demodulation circuit to get optimum results; and very elaborate demodulators are needed for some pulse modulation systems, particularly PCM.

Comparison of different modulation systems

1. Amplitude modulation (AM)

Advantages

- Comparatively simple modulation circuits.
- Very simple demodulation.
- Calculations of bandwidth easy.

Disadvantages

- Much transmitter power is wasted because only one sideband is needed to carry information, the carrier and the other sideband being unused by the receiver.
- Signals caused by electrical storms or by unsuppressed electrical machines cause interference with the received signals.

The range and efficiency of AM transmissions can be much improved by using *single sideband* (SSB), or *suppressed carrier*, systems. In these systems, either an arrangement of filters or a different type of modulator circuit at the transmitter is used either to remove one of the carrier sidebands almost completely, or to reduce the amplitude of the carrier, or both. The penalty which has to be paid is a much more complex demodulator. These systems have never been used in general broadcasting, therefore, but they are commonly used in high-grade communications systems and by radio amateurs.

2. Frequency modulation

Advantages

- Simple modulation circuits.
- Carrier amplitude constant, so that transmitter range can be greater than with AM.
- Freedom from interference because interference signals do not alter the frequency of the transmitted signal.

Disadvantages
- Complex demodulator circuits.
- Wide bandwidth requirement.

3. Pulse modulation

Advantages

- Simple modulation circuits.
- Often the only type of modulation possible with some oscillators.
- Multiplex transmission made possible.

Disadvantages

- Very wide bandwidth needed, so that pulse modulation can only be used with carriers of very high frequency.

Measurement of modulation

The extent of modulation of an AM transmission is measured by reference to its *percentage depth of modulation*. Take the waveform of Figure 9.5. The amplitudes of the modulation peak (V_p) and of the modulation trough (V_t) are measured, and the percentage depth is given by the expression:

$$\frac{V_p - V_t}{V_p + V_t} \times 100\%$$

The value of this expression must never be allowed to exceed 100 per cent if the signal is to be saved from severe distortion.

Frequency modulation

The concept of depth of modulation for FM is rather complex and based on the ratio of carrier frequency change to the frequency of the modulating signal that

Table 9.1 Public service broadcast standards

Service	Modulation	Typical IF	Bandwidth
LW/MW radio	AM	465/470 kHz	9/10 kHz
VHF radio	FM	10.7 MHz	200 kHz
UHF TV (PAL)	AM (Vision)	39.5 MHz	5.5 MHz ⎱(8 MHz
	FM (Sound)	33.5 MHz	150 kHZ ⎰channels)

produced the change. The term *deviation* is used to describe any change or deviation in carrier frequency from its mean or unmodulated value. The so called modulation index is given by:

$$\text{Mod. index} = \frac{\text{Carrier frequency deviation}}{\text{Modulating frequency}}$$

and thus varies considerably. However a limiting value is specified for any FM system as the *deviation ratio* which is given by:

$$\text{Deviation ratio} = \frac{\text{Maximum carrier frequency change allowed}}{\text{Maximum modulating frequency allowed}}$$

For the European VHF radio service the deviation has been standardized at ±75 kHz.

In all FM broadcasts, the modulation index has a value considerably in excess of unity. By contrast with an AM transmission, however, no sudden change of waveshape can be caused by over-modulation, whereas with AM, a single modulating frequency generates only a single pair of side frequencies in the complex wave. With FM each single modulating frequency generates many sideband pairs. The FM bandwidth is constant, irrespective of the modulation frequency or amplitude, so that a low modulating frequency gives rise to a larger number of sideband pairs than does a higher modulating frequency.

Transmitter and receiver block diagrams

Figure 9.16 shows the block diagram of an AM transmitter. The audio signal is derived from the transducer – in this case a *microphone* which converts sound waves into electrical signals. The *AF amplifier* amplifies these feeble signals (they have an amplitude of one millivolt or less) to the amplitude required to modulate the carrier wave.

At the same time, an oscillator tuned to a high radio frequency generates a carrier wave. It may be followed by several other stages of frequency multiplica-

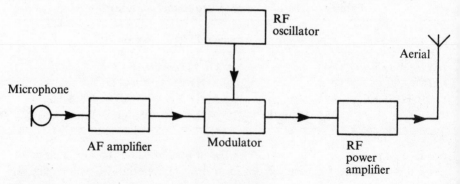

Figure 9.16   Block diagram of AM transmitter

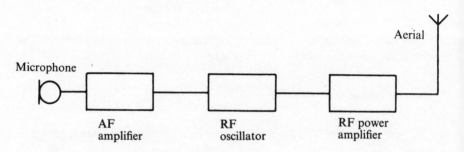

Figure 9.17   Block diagram of FM transmitter

tion and amplification, but eventually carrier wave and audio signal are combined in the *modulator* which produces at its output a modulated RF signal.

This modulated RF signal is amplified in the *power amplifier* (PA) to produce a signal which can feed the aerial (the output transducer of the transmitter) with an alternating voltage and a large alternating current. The PA is required because the aerial consumes much power, dissipating it in the form of radio waves of electromagnetic radiation.

Apart from the audio amplifier, every amplifying stage of the transmitter is tuned to operate at the frequency of transmission.

Filter circuits ensure that the signal fed to the aerial contains only the desired output carrier and its sidebands.

The FM transmitter

Reference to Figure 9.17 will show that the audio signal is still used to modulate the carrier, as in the AM transmitter, but now in such a way as to cause changes

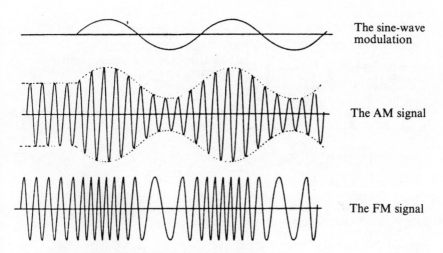

The sine-wave modulation

The AM signal

The FM signal

Figure 9.18   The AM and FM signals compared

Table 9.2   Summary of effects of modulation

	AM	FM
Amplitude of modulating signal	Varies carrier *amplitude*	Varies carrier *frequency*
Frequency of modulating signal	Controls *rate of change of amplitude*	Controls *rate of change of frequency*
System constant	*Carrier frequency*	*Carrier amplitude*

in its *frequency* rather than in its amplitude. The frequency-modulated wave is then amplified in the power stages before being radiated by the aerial system.

Figure 9.18 presents a graphic comparison of the AM and FM waveforms.

Table 9.2 offers a convenient summary of the detailed effects of both types of modulation.

Figure 9.19 shows the block diagram of an *AM receiver* typical of a transistor radio intended for medium or long-wave reception. Like practically all radio receivers, its operation is based on the superheterodyne (*superhet*) principle.

In a superhet receiver the incoming signal, whatever its frequency, has that frequency converted to an *intermediate frequency* (IF), which is *lower than the radio frequency*. The purpose of this conversion is to make amplification easier, for it is simpler to design a high-gain amplifier which is tuned to a set frequency than one which needs to have its tuning altered whenever it is desired to receive another transmission. A superhet receiver carries only a few variable-tuned circuits, most of the amplification being carried in the IF amplifier.

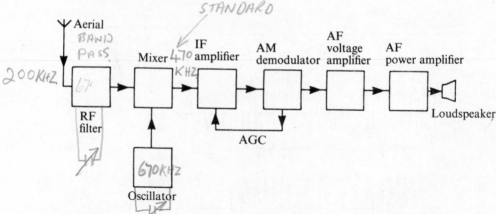

Figure 9.19   Block diagram of AM receiver

In Figure 9.19, the stage labelled RF filter selects the wanted signal from all the other signals picked up by the aerial. This filter therefore must have variable tuning. It acts also to reduce the amplitude of any oscillator frequency which might otherwise be re-radiated from the aerial.

The oscillator circuit also is variably tuned, but in such a way that its frequency is 465 kHz *higher* than that of the incoming signal. Pre-set capacitors called *trimmers* and *padders* maintain this frequency difference, which is the IF frequency, over the whole of the tuned range. The oscillator is said to be 'tracking the input correctly' when the frequency difference, or IF, remains correct over the full range.

The incoming signal and the oscillator sine-waves are mixed in the *mixer* stage, so producing two new frequencies which are also modulated. One of these new modulated frequencies is the IF, which is in this example 465 kHz – the difference between the frequencies of the oscillator and of the incoming signal. The second modulated frequency produced in the mixer stage is a signal whose frequency is equal to the *sum* of the frequencies of the oscillator and of the incoming signal, known as the image frequency.

The mixer also acts as a tuned amplifier – tuned to the frequency of the IF. For this reason, only the IF output is allowed to pass to the IF amplifier, all the other frequencies – incoming signal, oscillator sine-wave and the sum frequency – being blocked or rejected.

The *IF amplifier*, in its turn, greatly increases the amplitude of the IF signal, which itself now carries the same modulation as did the incoming signal.

The modulated and amplified IF signal is applied to the *AM demodulator*, which produces two outputs. One is the modulating signal itself, which is at audio frequency and free of any trace of the intermediate frequency; the other is a d.c. voltage *which is always proportional to the average amplitude of the IF signal*. When a weak or distant transmitter is being received, the incoming signal

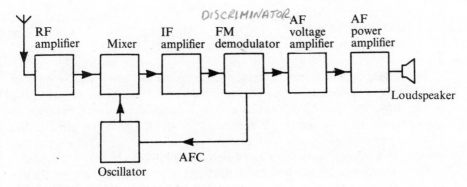

Figure 9.20 Block diagram of FM receiver

will produce at the mixer an IF signal of very low amplitude. Even after amplification in the mixer and IF amplifier stages, this amplitude may still be low.

On the other hand, a nearby or powerful transmitter might provide a signal that directly breaks through into the IF amplifier stages. This then causes interference or overloading. Both lead to distortion.

It is to minimize the effects of these two extremes that the d.c. produced in the AM demodulator is used, being fed back to control the gain of the IF amplifier itself. What happens is that a small-amplitude signal at the demodulator gives rise to a small d.c. feedback signal, which permits the IF amplifier to operate at full gain. A large amplitude signal at the demodulator gives rise to a large d.c. signal, which gives what is called *negative bias* to the IF amplifier and causes it to operate at much reduced gain.

By the use of this so-called *automatic gain control* (AGC) circuit, the signal at the demodulator is kept to an almost constant level even when there are great variations in the amplitudes of incoming signals.

The AF signal from the demodulator passes to an audio-frequency voltage amplifier incorporating a volume control which increases or decreases a.f. gain. This amplifier sometimes includes also a tone control, which increases or reduces the gain at low and high frequencies respectively. The AF signal is then fed to a power amplifier, which boosts it sufficiently to drive the output transducer – a loudspeaker.

Figure 9.20 shows an *FM receiver* whose working principles are similar. The superheterodyne principle is again used, but because of the much higher incoming frequency range (90–108) MHz and the greater bandwidth (about 200 kHz), an IF of 10.7 MHz is required.

Another difference is that a tuned RF amplifier is placed in series between the aerial input and the mixer stage. This has two effects:

(a)   To raise the amplitude of the desired RF signal well above the amplitude of unwanted interference.

(b) To prevent the oscillator frequency leaking back from the mixer to the aerial, from which it could cause severe interference for other receivers.

The mixer, oscillator and IF stages act in much the same way as do their equivalents in a medium-wave AM receiver. The demodulator, however, is a special FM type, for AM detectors cannot in normal operation produce an output from an FM signal. Moreover, it is essential that the circuit shall produce no varying output when the *amplitude* of the IF signal changes. Only changes in *frequency* form the wanted signal which has to be demodulated.

The d.c. output from the FM demodulator is of a type different from the d.c. output of the AM demodulator. When the FM demodulator is correctly adjusted, its d.c. output is zero when the IF is centred at the correct frequency – which means when the receiver is correctly tuned. The correct tuning of the FM receiver, however, depends on the correct tuning of the *oscillator*, so it is to the control of *oscillator frequency* that this correcting d.c. output from the FM demodulator is directed.

This arrangement is known as *automatic frequency control* (AFC). It is necessary because the frequency of a variable-frequency oscillator working in the range 100–120 MHz is very easily affected by small changes either of temperature or of supply voltage. The AFC voltage acts promptly to correct these small changes, so keeping the whole receiver tuned to the correct transmission frequency.

Perhaps the outstanding feature of all FM transmission systems is their so-called 'capture effect'. An FM receiver will lock on to the modulation of the slightly stronger of two signals of the same frequency and reproduce only the modulation of the stronger.

This efficient *selectivity* (as it is called), combined with the freedom which the FM system gives from interference caused by 'noise' from electrical storms or other electrical equipment, has led to FM being widely used in communications equipment, especially for mobile radio. The use of FM in stereo broadcasting is covered in Part 2 of this series.

Sub-carriers

More than one modulating signal at a time can be transmitted on a single carrier by making use of a *sub-carrier* (see multiplex operation).

A sub-carrier is a sine-wave whose frequency is greater than the normal frequency range of the signal, whether it be of audio or video frequency, which is to be transmitted. This sub-carrier can be modulated by one, or even two, signals at a time. The modulated sub-carrier and the other modulating signal are then both modulated on to the main carrier.

Both stereo sound broadcasts, which use a 38 kHz sub-carrier, and colour TV itself, which uses a 4.43 MHz sub-carrier, work on this principle.

Exercise 9.2
Using an AM/FM battery-operated portable receiver and an AM/FM signal generator, provide a suitable level of input signal at intermediate frequency to the mixer stage output. Using a double-beam oscilloscope, monitor the signals present at the input and output of the detector stage. Sketch these waveforms and compare their time and amplitude relationships. Switch both receiver and signal generator to FM and repeat the exercise. Again compare the waveforms as before, but also compare the AM and FM waveforms.

Test questions

9.1   The UK VHF FM radio service uses a maximum deviation of
(a) ± 9 kHz
(b) ± 75 kHz
(c) ± 150 kHz
(d) ± 200 kHz

9.2   On medium wave radio transmissions, AM is used instead of FM because of
(a) better sound quality
(b) less noise
(c) greater signal strength
(d) reduced bandwidth.

9.3   The circuit that is used to recover the information component from a modulated wave at a receiver is called
(a) an oscillator
(b) a modulator
(c) a detector
(d) a limiter.

9.4   In an AM system, the effect of varying the modulating voltage is to alter
(a) the depth of modulation
(b) the deviation
(c) the bandwidth
(d) the side frequencies.

9.5   Frequency modulation is preferred for applications that require
(a) low cost with simplicity
(b) simple demodulation with low bandwidth
(c) high fidelity with little interference

(d) where bandwidth is restricted.

9.6 The types of modulation used in the UK 625 line PAL television system
are

Video	Sound
(a) FM	FM
(b) FM	AM
(c) AM	FM
(d) AM	AM

10 Power supplies

Refer to syllabus section 06(003)

All electronic circuits need some sort of power supply – usually a steady (d.c.) voltage. A few circuits, however, need only a.c. as a supply, with no conversion to d.c.; while a handful more use an incoming signal to provide the power they need.

The electrical power required by a circuit is obtained by converting some form of energy into electrical energy. A source of energy is equivalent to a store of work. Given an appropriate energy-changing device, all forms of energy are mutually interchangeable. When energy is converted from one form into another, the inefficiencies result in the dissipation of the lowest form of energy – heat. Heat flows from a hot object to a cold one so that heat energy is never completely lost. This obeys two fundamental laws of physics, one that states that energy cannot be created or destroyed – just changed from one form into another; the other, that energy is always being converted to a less useful form.

Storage of significant quantities of electrical energy is at present impossible, so the large amounts of electrical energy which are present during thunderstorms are of no use to mankind. Instead, other forms of energy, principally the chemical energy contained in fuels, are converted into electrical forms as and when needed.

Batteries convert chemical energy into electrical energy without any intermediate stage of conversion to heat. Only a few chemical reactions can at present be harnessed in this way, though recent work on fuel cells has enabled electricity to be generated directly without any fuel having to be burnt to provide heat.

Batteries, however, though important as a source of electrical energy for electronic devices, represent only a tiny fraction of the total electrical energy which is generated. A much greater fraction of this energy – indeed most of all the energy we use – is obtained from generators driven by steam turbines. The steam is raised either by burning conventional fuel such as coal, gas or oil, or by nuclear reactions. Because rotating machinery is involved in the generator process (see Chapter 11), the most convenient form of electrical energy to produce is a.c., which is therefore used as the mains supply (in the USA, 'line supply') in practically every country in the world.

The generation of electricity from other sources such as sunlight, wind, waves, the tides or direct from heat is at the time of writing either inefficient or uneconomic, or both – save in a few applications (radio beacons, unmanned relay stations and space satellites, for example) for which low-powered equipment only is required.

Primary and secondary cells

A cell converts chemical energy directly into electrical energy. A collection of cells is called a *battery*. Cells may be connected in series to increase the voltage available or in parallel to increase the current capacity, but parallel connection is undesirable because it can lead to the rapid discharge of all cells if one becomes faulty.

Cells may be either primary or secondary cells. A primary cell is one that is ready to operate as soon as the chemicals composing it are put together. Once the chemical reaction is finished, the cell is exhausted and can only be thrown away. A secondary cell generally needs to be *charged* before it can be used. Its chemical reaction takes place in one direction during charging, and in the other direction during discharge (use) of the cell.

Most *primary cells* are of the zinc/carbon (Leclanché) type, of which a cross-section is shown in Figure 10.1. The zinc case is sometimes steel-coated to give extra protection. The ammonium chloride paste is an acidic material which gradually dissolves the zinc. The subsequent chemical action provides the energy from which the electrical voltage is obtained.

The purpose of the manganese dioxide mixture surrounding the carbon rod is to absorb hydrogen gas, a by-product of the chemical reaction. The hydrogen would otherwise gather on the carbon, insulating it so that no current could flow.

The zinc/carbon cell is suitable for most purposes for which batteries are used, having a reasonable shelf life and yielding a fairly steady voltage throughout a good working life.

Other types of cell such as alkaline manganese, mercury or silver oxide and

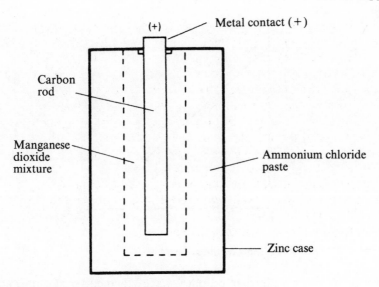

Figure 10.1   A typical (Leclanché) dry cell

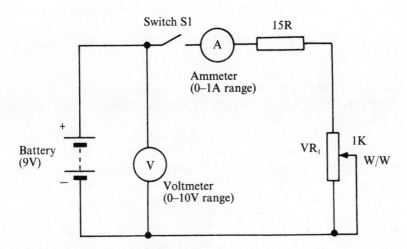

Figure 10.2   Diagram for Exercise 10.1

lithium are used in more specialized applications requiring high working currents, very steady voltage or very long life at low current drains. However, mercury based cells are not considered environmentally friendly when discarded unless they can be returned to the manufacturer.

Exercise 10.1

Connect the circuit of Figure 10.2 using a 9V transistor radio battery. Draw up

173

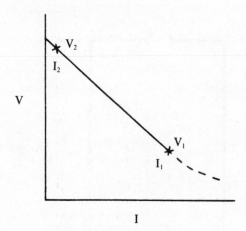

Figure 10.3   Output voltage against current

a table on to which readings of output voltage V and current I can be entered.

With the switch S1 open, note the voltmeter reading (using the 10V scale). Mark the current column 'zero' for this voltage reading. Then close S1 and adjust the variable resistor VR_1 until the current flow recorded on the current meter is 50mA. Note the voltage reading V at this level of current flow, and record both readings on the table. Open switch S1 again as soon as the readings have been taken.

Go on to make a series of readings at higher currents (75mA, 100mA, etc.) until voltage readings of less than 5V are being recorded.

Take care that for every reading S1 remains closed for only as long as is needed to make the reading.

Plot the readings you have obtained on a graph of output voltage against current. It should look like that shown in Figure 10.3.

Now pick from the table a pair of voltage readings – V_1 and V_2, with V_2 greater than V_1 – together with their corresponding current readings, I_1 and I_2, expressed in amperes. Work out the value of the following expression:

$$\frac{V_1 - V_2}{I_1 - I_2}$$

and you will get the internal resistance of the battery.

Towards the end of the useful life of a cell or battery, the value of its internal resistance rises. This causes the output voltage at the terminals of the cell or battery to drop below its normal value when current flows through the cell or battery – which is then said to have *poor regulation*. A voltage check with this cell or battery removed from the equipment will show a normal voltage rating, but the cell/battery should nevertheless be replaced.

The only useful check on the state of a cell or battery is a comparison of

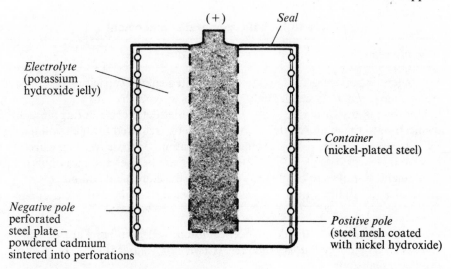

Figure 10.4 The nickel-cadmium cell

voltage reading *on load* (with normal current flowing) with the known on-load voltage of a fresh cell.

Until fairly recently, the term *secondary cell* meant either the type of lead-acid cell which is familiar as the battery in your car, or the nickel-iron-alkaline (NiFe) cell used in such applications as the powering of electric milk floats. In present-day electronics, both types have to some extent been superseded by the *nickel-cadmium* secondary (i.e., rechargeable) cell.

As a matter of interest, both types of alkaline cells (so-called because they use alkaline rather than acid electrolyte) were invented in the same year, 1900 – the nickel-iron cell by Edison in the USA, the nickel cadmium cell by Jungner in Sweden. Only recently, however, have the advantages of the nickel-cadmium cell been exploited. The active material cadmium (a metal akin to zinc), in powdered form, is pressed or *sintered* into perforated steel plates, which then form the negative pole of the cell. The positive pole is a steel mesh coated with solid nickel hydroxide. The electrolyte is potassium hydroxide (caustic potash), usually in jelly form (see Figure 10.4).

Nickel-cadmium cells are sealed in such a way that no liquids can be spilled from them, and they have a fairly long working life provided they are correctly used. They can deliver large currents, so can be used for equipment demanding higher power than could be supplied by primary cells. They have much longer life when they are rapidly discharged at intervals. Long periods of inactivity can cause the cells to fail, though it is often possible to restore their action by successive cycles of discharging and charging.

Unlike the lead-acid accumulator, the nickel-cadmium cell needs to be charged *at a constant current*. Specially-designed chargers must therefore be

175

Table 10.1   Battery-operated equipment

Advantages	Disadvantages
Equipment is portable. An ordinary battery is smaller and lighter than is any form of connection to the main supply. Safer to use – no high voltages being involved. Equipment, not have to be plugged in, requires no trailing leads.	Limited energy capacity. Voltage generally low. Batteries deteriorate during storage. Batteries required for high voltage operation, or to deliver high current flows, are heavier and more bulky than the equivalent equipment operated from the mains.

used. *On no account* should a nickel-cadmium cell ever be charged from a constant voltage type battery-charger as used for lead-acid cells, or from an ordinary mains power supply unit.

Solar cells

Although a number of materials are capable of generating photo-electric energy, silicon is the most popular. Solar cells are constructed from a matrix of silicon PN junctions. Each junction is typically five centimetres square and about half a millimetre thick, with the junction being formed very close to the upper surface. This is covered with a metallic grid formation to provide one contact and allow light to penetrate easily into the junction to generate the photo-voltaic potential. The back surface is covered with a metallic layer to provide a second low-resistance connection. Each cell is capable of generating a maximum open circuit voltage of 0.6 V, with a typical operating value of 0.4V. Such a cell will support a short circuit current of about 100 mA. Solar generators are constructed from a series parallel arrangement of individual cells and a panel of 1 square metre can easily provide upwards of 100 watts of power.

Large value capacitors

Capacitors with a value of about 1 to 5 Farads which can be charged to 5 volts through a high value of resistance, can support a small discharge current for many hours. Modern construction provides a device of only about 25 mm high with the same diameter, so that these can be used to provide a back-up power supply for circuits that need only a small current to maintain operation throughout short-duration power failures.

Table 10.1 lists the advantages and disadvantages of operating electronic

Table 10.2   Primary and secondary cells compared

Primary cells	Secondary cells
Low cost.	Expensive.
Small size.	Comparatively long life.
Short life.	Rechargeable.
Throw-away when exhausted.	Generally heavier than equivalent
Light weight.	primary cell.
Readily available.	Specialized products, less easily
	obtainable.

equipment by battery. Table 10.2 similarly compares primary and secondary cells.

Mains supplies

The cheapest method of operating any electronic circuit whose power consumption is more than a few milliwatts is by means of a *power supply unit* (PSU) drawing its energy from the a.c. mains supply. The purpose of a PSU is to raise or lower the mains supply voltage to an amplitude suitable for the application, and then to convert this a.c. voltage into a steady d.c. one. Sometimes additional circuits called *stabilizers are* needed to ensure that the d.c. output voltage remains steady even when mains voltage varies, or if the amount of current taken from the PSU is altered.

The voltage conversion is carried out by a *transformer* (see Chapter 11). A.c. voltage from the mains is applied to the primary of the transformer, and induces a voltage between the terminals of the transformer secondary. The value of this secondary voltage depends on the relative number of turns in the two windings. Most modern transistor equipment requires that the secondary voltage be lower than the primary voltage, the required voltage being usually within the range 6V to 50V.

The first stage in the conversion of the lowered a.c. voltage to d.c. is carried out by a *rectifier*, or series of rectifiers, which alter the wave-shape of the a.c. into one of the wave-shapes shown in Figure 10.5 – of which the *full-wave rectifier* arrangement is preferred for most applications.

The result of rectification is to produce the waveforms shown on the right-hand side of Figure 10.5 which are of a voltage in one polarity only. To convert this into smooth d.c., a *reservoir capacitor and filter* must be used. The reservoir capacitor is charged by the current from the rectifier(s), and supplies current to the circuit every time the voltage output from the rectifiers drops. In this the waveform is *smoothed* into d.c. plus a small amount of remaining a.c. called

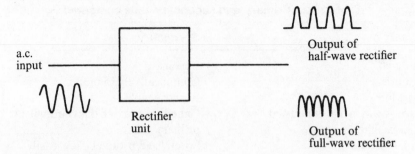

Figure 10.5 Rectifer action

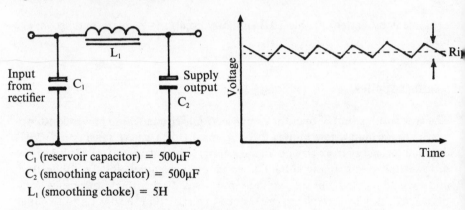

C_1 (reservoir capacitor) = 500µF

C_2 (smoothing capacitor) = 500µF

L_1 (smoothing choke) = 5H

Figure 10.6 Ripple voltage and a typical filter

ripple. See Figure 10.6.

This ripple is almost zero when only a little current is taken from the PSU, but it increases considerably when more current is taken. If it becomes unacceptably high, a larger value of reservoir capacitor must be used, or additional filter stages must be added.

Half-wave and full-wave rectification – a comparison

When no load current is taken from a rectifier circuit, the output from a half-wave circuit, as measured by a d.c. voltmeter, will be identical to that from a full-wave circuit supplied with the same d.c. voltage. When a load current flows, however, the output voltage of a half-wave rectifier circuit will drop by a greater amount than will that of the full-wave rectifier circuit, unless a much larger value of reservoir capacitor is used.

The a.c. ripple which appears when the load current is taken from a rectifier circuit will be at mains frequency when the rectifier is a half-wave one, but at

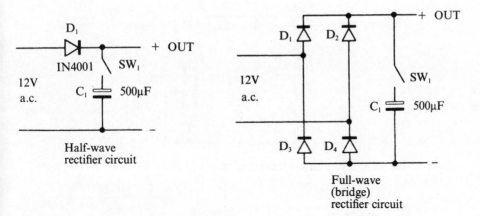

Figure 10.7 Diagram for Exercise 10.2

twice mains frequency when the rectifier is a full-wave circuit (see Figure 10.5). When the load current taken is very large, the voltage output from a half-wave supply will fall to about half the value of that from a full-wave supply connected to the same a.c. voltage.

The regulation of neither type of supply is good, though adequate for many purposes. Regulation, you will recall, is the term used to quantify the drop of output voltage which occurs when load current is taken from the supply circuit. A perfectly regulated supply would have constant output voltage whatever the noted load current.

Failure in any part of a PSU is easy to diagnose. Symptoms are complete loss of output voltage, a drop in output voltage, excessive ripple or unusually poor regulation. Complete failure can be caused by a blown fuse or by an o/c transformer winding. A short-circuit in a half-wave rectifier will also bring output to zero. A short circuit winding in the transformer will, in addition, generate excessive heat.

A drop in voltage, usually accompanied by excessive ripple can be caused by the failure of one of the rectifiers in a full-wave set, or by an o/c reservoir capacitor. Poor regulation can also be caused by an o/c reservoir capacitor, or by a diode developing unduly high resistance.

Exercise 10.2

Connect the a.c. rectifier/reservoir circuits shown in Figure 10.7. (Note that these are intended for use with 12V a.c. supplies only – they must on no account be connected to the mains.)

Use the a.c. voltage range of a multimeter to set the a.c. input to 12V, and measure the output voltage of each circuit. Note down the readings under appropriate headings. Note also the output readings when the reservoir capacitors are temporarily disconnected. Compare the ripple amplitude and frequency

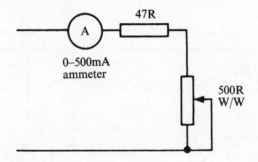

Figure 10.8   Load circuit for Exercise 10.2

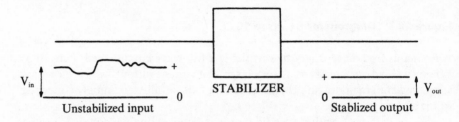

Figure 10.9   The action of a voltage stabilizer

using an oscilloscope.

Now connect to each output in turn the load circuit of Figure 10.8. Measure the output voltages at various load currents from 50mA to 200mA for both rectifier circuits, and draw up a table of output voltage and load current.

Draw a graph of output voltage plotted against load current for each type of rectifier circuit. Calculate a figure for internal resistance, using the method explained in Exercise 10.1.

To keep the output voltage of a rectifier circuit steady despite variations in the a.c. mains input or in the amount of current drawn at the output, it is sometimes possible to use a subsequent *stabilizer circuit*. This can only be done however, if the voltage output from the filter is several volts higher than the voltage output required from the stabilizer itself. A stabilizer cannot restore lost voltage. It can only control the voltage at its output; and it cannot operate at all if the voltage from the filter stage is lower than the voltage setting of the stabilizer (see Figure 10.9).

A fixed-voltage stabilizer circuit will produce its fixed output voltage only if the input voltage never falls below the minimum needed to operate the stabilizer. A *variable-output stabilizer* is a circuit whose steady d.c. output is controlled by the setting of a potentiometer but which will remain stabilized at whatever voltage is set by that potentiometer. Again, stabilization is possible

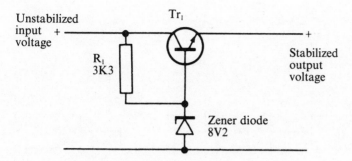

Figure 10.10   Diagram for Exercise 10.3

only if the input d.c. voltage is high enough to allow the stabilizer to function correctly. If the input voltage is inadequately smoothed or is too low to permit correct stabilizer action, there will be no true stabilization.

In the event of suspected stabilizer failure, the waveform and voltage of the input should be checked before any other steps are taken.

Exercise 10.3

Construct the stabilizer circuit shown in Figure 10.10. TR1 is of the type known as MJE3055, which is housed in a convenient flat-packed casing. Bolt the metal face of the transistor through the hole in the casing to a 6cm-square sheet of 14-gauge aluminium or to a pre-shaped heat-sink. The other two components, the resistor R1 and the Zener diode ZD1, can be mounted on tagstrip or matrix board.

Connect the stabilizer as shown in Figure 10.10 to the full-wave rectifier/reservoir circuit, and switch on. Measure the output voltage resulting from various current flows, as explained in Exercise 10.2. Find a value for the internal resistance of the complete circuit under test.

Stabilizer circuits are more liable to failure than are simple rectifier/reservoir supplies because of their additional active components. In the simple circuit shown, the failure would be indicated either by zero output or by an unstabilized output at about the same voltage as the input.

Circuits for stabilizing a.c. also exist – not all of them entirely electronic. Saturable transformer stabilizers consist of specially-wound transformers whose output can be controlled by a d.c. circuit. The d.c. is provided by rectifying part of the a.c. output so that the output becomes self-regulating. *Take care when you are either connecting or disconnecting such stabilizers, for they contain charged capacitors.*

Stabilizers of this type are commonly used in photographic processing plants to regulate the supply to enlarger lamps so that colour processing becomes more consistent.

Thyristor or triac a.c. stabilizers use electronic switching components to regulate the average power of a.c. They will be described in some detail in

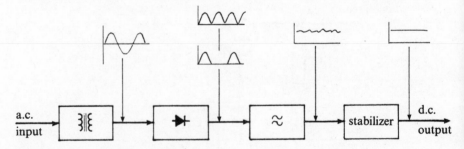

Figure 10.11   A power supply system

Volume 2 of this series.

Note that all types of a.c. stabilizer somewhat distort the shape of the mains waveform, so that it is normal to connect filter circuits to both the input and output leads of these stabilizers to minimize the transmission of radio frequency interference (RFI).

Exercise 10.4

Construct the power supply system shown in Figure 10.11 in progressive stages, starting with a suitable resistive load connected across the mains transformer secondary winding, taking specific note of the correct polarity of electrolytic capacitors. Using a multi-range meter and oscilloscope, study and sketch the voltage levels and waveforms obtained. Measuring the ripple amplitude and d.c. level. Repeat these steps as the rectifier, filter and stabilizer units are added.

Suitable component values are as follows:

- Transformer, mains input, 12V at 100 mA secondary winding.
- Reservoir and smoothing capacitors, 500 μF, 50V d.c. working.
- Smoothing choke, 5 Henries.
- Stabilizer, 12V input, 8–10V output at 100 mA.
- Suitable load, 82Ω 5W resistor. If not available, a 15 watt mains lamp can be used as a substitute.

Test questions

10.1   A cell or a battery converts
(a) heat energy into electrical energy
(b) electrical energy into light energy
(c) electrical energy into chemical energy
(d) chemical energy into electrical energy.

10.2   If the load current drawn from an unstabilized power supply is initially small and then increased, the output voltage will

(a) decrease initially and then remain constant
(b) remain constant
(c) increase
(d) decrease.

10.3   A primary cell
(c) can be recharged indefinitely
(b) has no resistance
(c) must be discarded when exhausted
(d) provides a high current.

10.4   Full-wave rectification as compared to half-wave rectification, provides
(a) more current
(b) higher ripple frequency
(c) lower voltage
(d) poorer regulation.

10.5   The action of a stabilizer circuit is to
(a) reduce the original voltage when current is drawn
(b) amplify the d.c. voltage from the rectifier
(c) raise the output voltage when current is drawn
(d) maintain a steady voltage well below the maximum value.

10.6   A nickel-cadmium (NiCad) cell must be recharged
(a) from a source of constant current
(b) from a low impedance source
(c) from a source of constant voltage
(d) from a high impedance source.

11 Magnetism and electromagnetic appliances

Refer to syllabus section 07(003)

When a quantity of iron filings is sprinkled on to a sheet of paper under which is placed a bar magnet, it is well known that the filings will arrange themselves into a definite pattern, called a *flux pattern*. This flux pattern is a map of the direction and strength of the forces which are exerted on the iron filings by reason of the proximity of the magnet. See Figure 11.1.

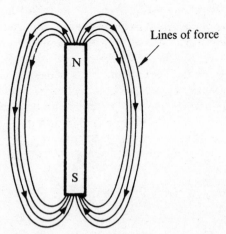

Figure 11.1   The flux pattern around a bar magnet

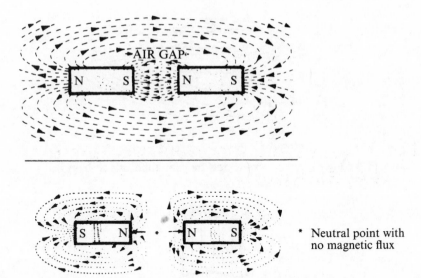

* Neutral point with
no magnetic flux

Figure 11.2   The flux patterns around two adjoining magnets

These forces exert their influence without any physical contact between the magnet and the iron filings. The general name for a force of such a type is a *field force*. The flux pattern, therefore, is a map of the magnetic field of the magnet. In this map, the direction in which needle-shaped filings point shows the direction of the field force being exerted, and the density of filings (i.e., the number of filings packed into a given area) indicates the strength of the field in that region.

(It is better, by the way, to think of the *lines of force* which go to make up a flux pattern as having rather irregular and ill-defined outlines. This is more representative of the actual shape of the flux pattern revealed by the distribution of a scattering of iron filings on a piece of paper subject to the influence of a magnet than are the idealized patterns seen in text-books.)

The pattern of the field which exists around a magnet can be changed in several ways. Figure 11.2 shows how the flux pattern appears when two magnets are present in proximity to one another. With both magnets aligned in the same north–south direction, the pattern is as shown in (a). When one of the magnets is reversed, the pattern alters to that shown in (b).

The shape of flux patterns is governed by two rules:

1.   The patterns act as if they were lines of force carrying a magnetic flux (or 'magnetic current') in the direction indicated by a compass needle.
2.   The flux lines become closely spaced together when they are physically near magnetic material – so indicating a strong field – but more widely spaced elsewhere, where the field is weaker.

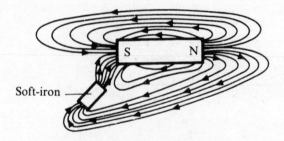

Soft-iron

Figure 11.3   Flux lines concentrated by presence of soft-iron rod

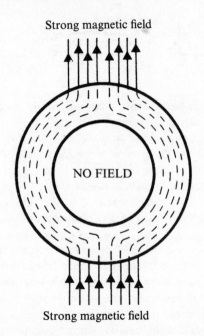

Strong magnetic field

NO FIELD

Strong magnetic field

Figure 11.4   A soft magnetic material acting as a magnetic shield

The shape of a flux pattern is not noticeably altered by the presence in its neighbourhood of non-magnetic materials such as plastics, copper or aluminium. The presence of magnetic materials, however, causes the flux pattern to change as shown in Figure 11.3.

Certain materials, classed as *soft* magnetic materials, although they are not permanent magnets themselves nevertheless possess the ability to concentrate flux lines. Such materials (soft iron, Permalloy and Mu-metal are examples) can be used as magnetic screens. Figure 11.4 shows that a cylinder of soft magnetic material will have no flux pattern inside the cylinder even when a strong field is

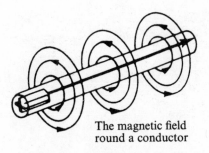

The magnetic field
round a conductor

Figure 11.5   The flux pattern around a current-carrying conductor

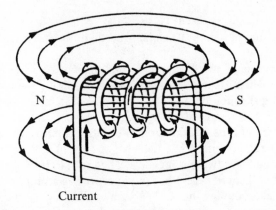

N   S

Current

Figure 11.6   The flux pattern around a current-carrying solenoid

present outside it. Such screening materials are used to shield cathode ray tubes
and other magnetically sensitive components from stray magnetic fields.

A soft magnetic material is readily magnetized by an outside force, but loses
that magnetism equally easily.

Permanent magnets are not the only source of magnetic flux. When an electric
current is passed through any conductor, a magnetic flux is created around the
conductor. The shape of this flux pattern (see Figure 11.5) is circular, unless it is
distorted by the presence of other magnetic material, and the pattern has no
start or finish points. This leads to the conclusion that all flux lines are, in fact,
closed lines without either start or finish.

A current-carrying conductor wound into the shape of a coil is called a
solenoid. The flux patterns of each part of a solenoid add to one another, so
producing the pattern shown in Figure 11.6. This pattern is similar to that of a
bar magnet save that the shape of the flux pattern inside the coil can now be
seen.

The addition of a soft magnetic material as a core inside a coil greatly

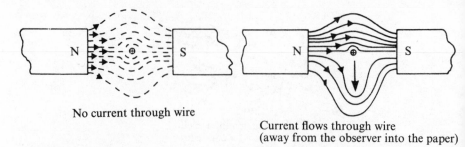

No current through wire

Current flows through wire
(away from the observer into the paper)

Figure 11.7   What happens when current flows through a wire in a magnetic field

concentrates the flux pattern at its ends – and therefore, presumably, inside the core also.

The concentration of the flux pattern means that a coil becomes a much stronger magnet when it has a soft magnetic core – though only for as long as current is flowing through the wire of the coil. A suitable coil material can in practice increase the strength of a magnetic field several thousand times.

Another important type of alteration in the flux pattern of a magnet occurs when a wire placed in a magnetic field has a current flowing through it. In Figure 11.7, N and S are two bar magnets. The little circle with a cross inside it which lies between them represents a conductor wire seen end on – that is to say, with one of its ends running into the paper away from you, and the other end running out of the paper towards your eye. When an electric current is passed through the wire, it will be seen that the flux pattern between the magnets becomes distorted.

In these circumstances, a magnetic force is exerted on the wire itself, acting at right angles to the wire and also at right angles to the flux lines. The direction in which this force is exerted can be remembered by using the so-called *left-hand rule for a conductor*. The thumb and first two fingers of the left hand are extended at right angles to one another, as pictured in Figure 11.8. The first finger then points in the direction of the flux (N→S); the second finger shows the direction of current flow (*positive to negative*); while the thumb points along the direction of the magnetic force exerted on the wire.

The force exerted between a flux pattern and a wire-carrying current is the principle on which the electric motor works. When current flows through the coil of wire shown in cross-section in Figure 11.9, there will be exerted on the ends of the coil forces which are equal but opposite in direction. The coil will therefore pivot about its central axis. This rotation will only continue, however, until the plane of the coil lies at 90° with the flux (in what is called its *neutral position*). In this position no force is acting to cause rotation because the coil is now aligned with its flux pattern.

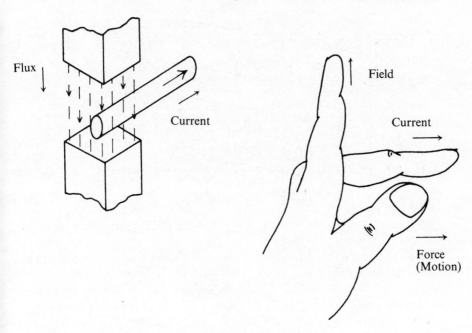

Figure 11.8   The left-hand rule for a conductor

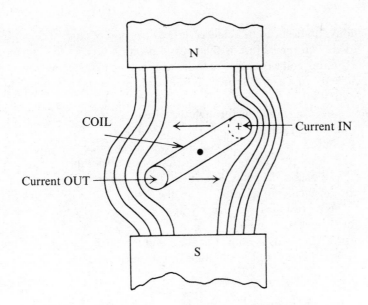

Figure 11.9   The forces acting on a coil (viewed end-on)

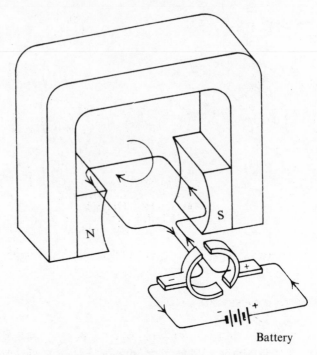

Figure 11.10   The principle of the d.c. motor

Continuous rotation can be achieved if the direction of current flow through the coil of wire is reversed just as the neutral position is reached. The momentum of the rotating coil will carry it a little way past the neutral position, and the reversed current again exerts a force on both ends of the coil which acts to keep the coil rotating.

The direction of current flow through the wire is constantly switched with the aid of a rotary switch called a *commutator*. (See Figure 11.10).

An electric motor with a single coil and two-segment commutator does not run at a uniform speed. The coil moves fastest when it is in the plane of the flux and slowest as it passes the neutral position. To ensure smoother running – and to avoid the problem of 'sticking' when the motor will not start if the coil happens to be at rest near its neutral position – several coils and pairs of commutator segments are used.

A set of revolving coils is known as the *armature* of the motor. The magnet (which may be either a permanent magnet or an electromagnet) is known as the *field*.

Magnetic flux is caused by the movement of electrons, which may be the movement through a conductor (electric current) or the spinning movement within the atoms which occurs in permanent magnetic materials.

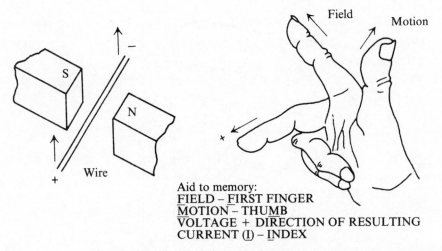

Aid to memory:
FIELD – FIRST FINGER
MOTION – THUMB
VOLTAGE + DIRECTION OF RESULTING
CURRENT (I) – INDEX

Figure 11.11 **The right-hand rule for finding the polarity of an induced voltage**

Application to moving coil meter

The moving coil meter uses a modification of the concept shown in Figure 11.10 to produce an indication of the d.c. current flowing through the coil. In this case, the coil is wound on a former and mounted in bearings but with a pointer attached. Current is fed to the coil through a pair of spiral springs which act to cause the coil to take up a zero position with zero current flowing. When a current flows through the coil, the resulting magnetic field interacts with that of the permanent magnet system to produce a deflection of the coil proportional to the current flowing in it, the pointer taking up an equilibrium position when the magnetic force is just balanced by the mechanical force of the springs.

Electromagnetic induction

An exactly reverse effect to what has been described above is known as *electromagnetic induction*. When the flux pattern around a conductor is changed *by moving the wire through the flux*, a voltage is generated between the ends of the wire. This induced voltage is greatest when the direction of the flux and the movement of the wire are at right angles to one another. This is the basic generator principle.

The polarity of the voltage induced can be remembered by the *right-hand rule* illustrated in Figure 11.11. *Note.* It is of interest to note that the direction of the currents for the left-hand and right-hand rules are opposite for the same directions of motion and fluxfield (see transformer induction, next section). The

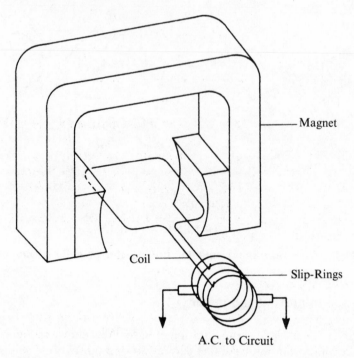

Magnet

Coil

Slip-Rings

A.C. to Circuit

Figure 11.12   The principle of the a.c. generator, using slip-rings

first two fingers and the thumb of the right hand are extended at right angles to one another. The first finger is pointed in the direction of the field of the magnet (N to S), and the thumb in the direction of the motion of the wire. The second finger then indicates the end of the wire which is positive.

This principle of motional induction is used to generate electricity by means of a device called an *alternator*. Figure 11.12 shows a simple alternator, basically of the same construction as an electric motor but with the commutator replaced by *slip-rings*. These slip-rings do not reverse connections. The waveform produced when the alternator is set spinning is a sine-wave whose voltage reaches maximum when the wire of the coil is momentarily moving at right angles to the flux, and zero at the instant when the wire of the coil is moving in line with (i.e. parallel to) the flux direction. The reversal of polarity is caused by the fact that the wire during its rotation must cut across the flux lines in one direction for half of its rotation and in the opposite direction for the other half.

The voltage, both r.m.s. and peak-to-peak, produced by an alternator increases as the speed of rotation increases. Large voltage outputs can be obtained by using large magnetic fields and many turns of wire in the rotating coil. The frequency of the a.c. output is determined entirely by the speed of the spinning coil and the number of poles of the magnet.

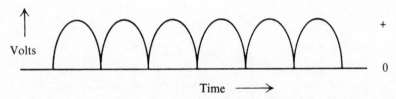

Figure 11.13   Output waveform of a generator connected to a commutator

If the slip-rings are replaced by a commutator, the waveform generated will be that shown in Figure 11.13 which will be recognized as full-wave rectified a.c. Alternators fitted with several coils and slip-rings generate *multi-phase a.c.*, each output wire carrying a sine-wave which is out of phase with all the others.

A d.c. generator using several coils and commutator segments, however, produces a reasonably smooth d.c. output.

Transformer induction

It is also possible to generate a voltage by induction without any mechanical motion. If the strength of the flux surrounding a conductor is varied, a voltage will be induced in the conductor. This effect, called *transformer induction*, is responsible for the very important electrical effect known as *inductance*.

When a current is made to flow through a coil of wire, or to cease flowing through it, the flux lines around the coil will respectively expand or collapse. This variation in the flux lines at once induces a voltage in the coil itself – *and this induced voltage is always so directed that it opposes the change of current flow.*

When, for example, a coil is connected to a battery, the induced voltage acts to oppose the battery voltage. When the coil is disconnected from the battery, the induced voltage will *aid* battery voltage.

Both of these effects, which are illustrated in Figure 11.14, are momentary, lasting only for the period during which current flow through the coil is changing. If, however, the current through the coil is an alternating one which is continually changing, an induced voltage will *always* be present. This induced voltage is also alternating, and so acts to oppose the flow of current, *making the coil behave as if it possessed greater resistance to a.c. than for d.c.*

Because it is the coil itself which induces the voltage opposing its own current flow, the opposing voltage is called an *e.m.f. of self-induction* or back e.m.f. The size of the induced voltage depends on the rate at which the flow of current changes, and on the shape and size of the coil. These 'geometrical' factors, shape and size, are measured by the quantity called inductance, which is measured in units of *Henries* (H). A coil has an inductance of 1 Henry when a rate of change

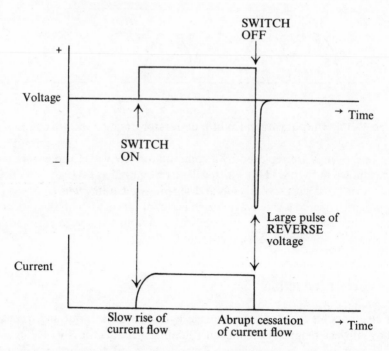

Figure 11.14   The effect of inductance when current is switched ON and OFF

of current of one ampere per second causes an induced voltage of 1 volt.

In practical work, the smaller units of *milliHenries* (mH) and *microHenries* (μH) are more useful. A few centimetres of straight wire will have an inductance of less than 1μH. Even a coil used to tune a medium-wave radio will only have an inductance of some 650μH. An iron-cored choke intended to act as a high impedance to audio signals might typically have an inductance of 50mH. Only a very large coil wound on a large laminated iron core would have an inductance which needed to be measured in Henries.

Any coil or inductor possesses also a property called reactance to signal currents. This reactance, measured in ohms and abbreviated as X_L, is defined in a similar way for a capacitor (see Chapter 6) as the value of:

$$\frac{\text{Signal voltage across the coil}}{\text{Signal current through the coil}}$$

Figure 11.15 shows how reactance varies with (a) inductance and (b) frequency. The reactance of a coil is thus proportional to both inductance and frequency. A coil can therefore present negligible resistance to d.c., but a large resistance to a.c.

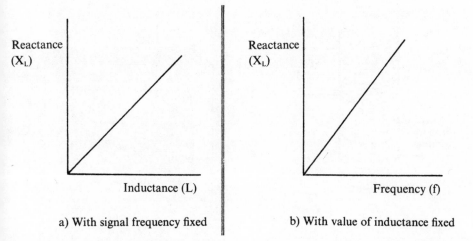

a) With signal frequency fixed

b) With value of inductance fixed

Figure 11.15   How inductive reactance varies with (a) value of inductance and (b) signal frequency

Transformer action

The changing flux around a coil carrying a changing current can also induce a voltage in another coil. This is the principle on which works the *transformer*, an appliance of which extensive use is made in electricity and electronics. A simple transformer, pictured in Figure 11.16, consists of two coils wound on a common core. When the current through one coil (the *primary winding*) changes, a voltage is induced in the other winding (the *secondary winding*).

Exercise 11.1

Connect a 100 mH choke in series with a resistor of about 5 KΩ across the output of an audio signal generator. Apply a constant level of signal at frequencies ranging from 100 Hz to 10 kHz and measure the signal voltage developed across the choke. (An Avo 8 or similar meter is suitable.) Plot the output voltages against a base of frequency. Explain why this graph has a similar characteristic to those shown in Figure 11.15.

Mutual inductance is said to exist between the windings; and it is equally true that a changing current passed through the secondary winding will cause a voltage to be induced in the primary winding. This will be more easily understood if the cross-section of a strip of transformer core and its windings illustrated in Figure 11.17 is studied. The primary and secondary windings of a transformer are there shown to be in close physical proximity to one another.

One of the principal functions of a transformer is to pass signals from one circuit to another without any connection other than the magnetic flux existing between the two circuits.

A transformer can also achieve a *step-up* or *step-down* of alternating voltage

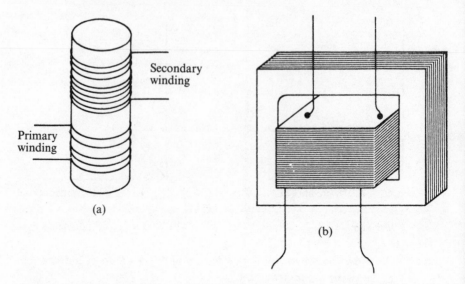

Figure 11.16   (a) Transformer principle; (b) a typical small transformer

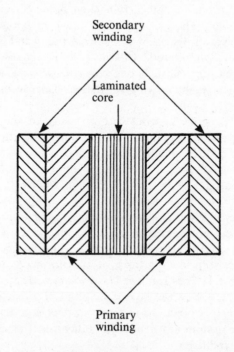

Figure 11.17   Cross-section of the windings on a transformer core

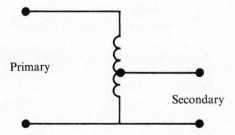

Figure 11.18   The auto-transformer

which is governed by the ratio of the number of turns of wire comprising each of its two windings. For a given a.c. voltage across the primary winding (V_p), the voltage across the secondary winding will be

$$V_p \frac{N_s}{N_p},$$

where N_s is the number of turns in the secondary winding and N_p the number of turns in the primary winding of the signals. Also, assuming no power loss between primary and secondary, the current ratio I_p/I_s will be equal to N, the turns ratio.

The construction of a transformer core depends on the frequency range of the signals which the transformer is designed to handle. For the lowest audio frequencies, a large core of soft magnetic material in the form of thin laminations is enough (see again Figure 11.17). At higher frequencies, ferrite dust cores are required to diminish the magnetic losses which arise in metal cores when high-frequency signals pass through them. At the highest frequencies for which coils are wound, no metal core material is acceptable. Coils have either to be wound on plastic formers, or they are made self-supporting.

The auto-transformer

The so-called *auto-transformer* makes common use of part of one of its windings to serve as both primary and secondary of the device as a whole. As will be seen from Figure 11.18, it closely resembles diagrammatically a tapped inductor and this resemblance indeed carries through to its physical appearance.

The auto-transformer behaves exactly as does the transformer just described, except that it provides no d.c. isolation between its primary and secondary windings.

The ratios of voltage, current and resistance (impedance) in the auto-transformer are identical to those in the ordinary transformer, where it has been seen that the equation for finding the turns ratio (N) is:

$$N = \frac{\text{Number of turns on primary}}{\text{Number of turns on secondary}}$$

The same equation is equally valid for the auto-transformer.

A commonly-used type of auto-transformer having a tap which can be continuously varied between a range of zero to some 130 per cent of the nominal voltage available is called a *Variac*. It is useful in circuits in which the voltage needs to be set precisely to a known value.

Exercise 11.2

Connect the output of an audio signal generator set to a frequency of 1 kHz to the primary winding of a small audio transformer having a turns ratio of 5:1. Terminate the secondary winding with a resistance load of 3 to 5 ohms. Using a multi-range meter (Avo Model 8 or similar), measure both the primary and secondary voltages. Break the primary and secondary circuits to allow the addition of the meters in series so that the currents can be measured. Compare the resulting voltage and current ratios.

Test questions

11.1   The cores of electromagnets are usually made from
(a) steel
(b) nickel
(c) soft iron
(d) hard iron.

11.2   When two permanent magnets with like poles are placed close to each other, the effect is to
(a) attract each other
(b) repel each other
(c) induce a current into each other
(d) generate heat.

11.3   When a current flows in a wire that is placed in a magnetic field there is a mechanical force exerted on the wire. The direction of this force is
(a) the same as that of the magnetic field
(b) the same as the current
(c) at right angles to both field and current
(d) opposite to the direction of the current.

11.4   A sine-wave voltage is generated when a coil
(a) revolves in a magnetic field
(b) moves in line with the magnetic field
(c) moves in a straight line across the magnetic flux
(d) is held stationary.

11.5   When a current that has been flowing through an inductor is suddenly cut off, there is a
(a) large pulse of voltage
(b) small pulse of current
(c) large pulse of current
(d) continuous voltage.

11.6   A transformer has 1000 turns in its primary winding and 2000 turns in its secondary. It will give
(a) 20V d.c. output for 10V d.c. input
(b) 10V d.c. output for 20V d.c. input
(c) 20V a.c. output for 10V a.c. input
(d) 10V a.c. output for 20V a.c. input

12 Some non-electrical physical principles

Refer to syllabus sections 07(008 to 010) and 04(4.1)

Although the flow of electrons through an electrical circuit must be the main concern of any student of electronics, there are other physical principles which need to be known and understood before a full understanding of electronics can be attained. The units in which energy and power, for example, are measured are derived from mechanical science; and these same units of *joules* and *watts* are applied to the generation and dissipation of heat energy. Since the power output of an amplifier is controlled by the rate at which its wasted heat can be dissipated, some knowledge of the principles of heat transfer is important. The understanding of how television works demands some acquaintance with the nature of light; and several other instances of equal importance could be quoted.

The mechanical units of most consequence are those of *mass, force, work* and *power*.

The *mass* of an object is often confused with its weight. Mass is a measurement of the quantity of material contained in an object, and the unit of mass is the *kilogram* (kg). Sub-divisions of the kilogram – the gram (g, which equals 1/1000 kg) and the *milligram* (mg) – are often used – with the *microgram* (μg) reserved for very small masses. The *weight* of an object on the other hand, is a measure of the force exerted on it by gravity, which will vary as the object is moved from one place to another on the Earth's surface – particularly if the object is taken up a high mountain or down to a steep depression below sea-

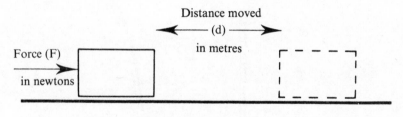

Work done = F × d (in joules)

Figure 12.1   An example of mechanical work

level.

A *force* has the effect of accelerating or decelerating a mass, and the unit of force is the amount needed to accelerate a mass of 1 kg by 1 metre per second ($1 m/s^2$). This unit is termed the *newton*. Both the kilogram and the newton are frequently met in service instructions. Spring tensions, for example are measured in newtons; the masses of pick-up styli are quoted in milligrams. Spring balances calibrated in newtons are common, and sets of standard masses from 1 mg upwards are available so that masses can be compared with one another on a balance.

Mechanical work is done when a force causes movement in the direction in which the force is exerted. The amount of work done is the product of the force exerted times the distance moved. When the force is expressed in newtons and the distance in metres, the work done is measured in units of *joules*. One joule of work is done when a force of one newton causes the object to which the force is applied to move one metre. See Figure 12.1.

Joules are also used to measure any type of latent energy, such as, for example, the energy stored in a charged capacitor or in a fully-wound spring.

When energy is *released* or *changed from one form to another*, the rate at which the energy is released or changed is called *power*. Power is measured in watts. A power of one watt means that energy is being released or changed at the rate of one joule per second, i.e. 1 watt = 1 joule/second.

Heat

The quantity called *temperature* measures the level of heat just as voltages measure electrical potential. Heat will flow from a place at a high temperature to one at a low temperature, just as naturally as water flows downhill or electric current flows from a point at high voltage to one at low voltage.

Temperature is, for most practical purposes, measured on the *Celsius* (*not* the 'Centigrade') scale, in which 0°C represents the freezing point of water at sea level and 100°C its boiling point.

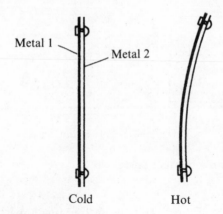

Cold   Hot

Figure 12.2   The bi-metal strip

Some electronic formulae require temperature to be expressed in the *absolute* (or *Kelvin*) scale. A temperature of 0 K (no degree sign) represents absolute zero. No lower temperature is even conceivable, either in theory or in practice. On the Kelvin scale, the freezing point of water is 273 K, and a comfortable 20°C room temperature is 293 K.

To convert Celsius degrees into Kelvin degrees, add 273 to the figure of Celsius temperature.

Temperature is measured by the effects it has on materials. Those include:

1. Gases, liquids and solids *expand* when temperature is increased.
2. The resistance of metals *increases* as temperature is increased.
3   The voltage across different metals in contact with one another (contact potential) *changes* as temperature is increased.

Thermometers and thermostats work by making the use of these effects. Conventional thermometers utilize the expansion and contraction of mercury: thermostats the expansion and contraction of solid bimetal strips (see Figure 12.2) A bi-metal strip bends in a predetermined direction as it is heated because one of the two metals of which it is composed expands, at a known rate, more than does the other.

Resistance thermometers operate by making use of the effect of temperature change on the level of electrical resistance which some materials display, and thermocouples take advantage of the voltage generated when junctions of dissimilar metals are heated.

It has been said that heat energy flows naturally from points at high tempera-ture to points at a lower temperature. The three known methods of heat energy transfer are *conduction, convection* and *radiation*. All three have applications in electronics. Heat is *conducted* through materials – most easily through metals,

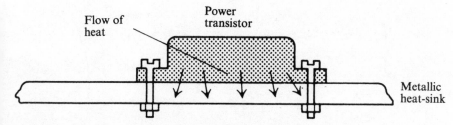

Figure 12.3   How heat is dissipated by conduction

hardly at all through gases. It is now known that heat is conducted best by materials which possess large numbers of free electrons – in other words, through materials which are also good electrical conductors.

Heat is also conducted by the movement of whole atoms, however; and some materials which are reasonably good conductors of heat are actually electrical insulators.

The importance of heat conduction in electronics is that this is the way in which all the heat generated in the inside of a transistor is dissipated to its case. The same heat is then often conducted even further away to a *heat-sink* – a formed metal slab on which the transistor is mounted. A thin mica washer is often sandwiched between the transistor and the heat-sink to provide electrical insulation while still allowing the conduction of heat. See Figure 12.3.

Because heat flows only from a high temperature to a low temperature, the interior of a working transistor is always at a higher temperature than is its case or the heat-sink itself.

Heat energy is transferred through gases by *convection*. A gas such as air gets heated when it comes into contact with a hot surface. This heated air expands, and acquires a density lower than that of the cold air surrounding it. The hot air therefore rises, carrying away heat with it, and allows cold air to take its place. A flow is therefore set up, with air moving past the hot object and removing heat from it in the process.

Convection is used to transfer the heat from transistors, resistors and other components to the air.

The action of a heat-sink is simply to present a larger surface to the air so as to make the removal of heat easier. Forced air cooling with the aid of fans greatly increases the rate at which heat can be removed. Water cooling is even more efficient.

Radiation does little to remove heat from objects unless they are at a really high temperature. The process of radiation involves the transfer of energy by means of electromagnetic waves; and though all objects radiate heat to some extent, the quantity radiated becomes significant only when the subject is at a temperature approaching red-heat.

Valves and cathode-ray tubes dissipate most of their heat by radiation.

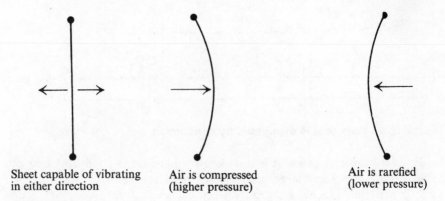

Sheet capable of vibrating
in either direction

Air is compressed
(higher pressure)

Air is rarefied
(lower pressure)

Figure 12.4   How a diaphragm sets up a sound wave

Solid-state electronic equipment does the job mainly by convection and conduction.

Sound

Sound is nothing more than a series of waves of pressure in the air caused by the vibration of a material which is in contact with the air. Imagine a thin flat sheet of material (it is called a *diaphragm*) which is in contact with air and which is made to vibrate. See Figure 12.4.

As the sheet vibrates, it alternately compresses and evacuates (or *rarefies*) the air next to it (and consequently the air molecules). Where the air is compressed, it exerts pressure on the air in contact with it. Where it is rarefied, a pressure is set up from the opposite direction. Every compression and rarefaction therefore spreads outwards from the source, forming a wave whose front moves at a speed of about 330 metres per second. See Figure 12.5.

As this wave moves through the air, a definite spacing is maintained between one pressure peak and the next. This distance is called a *wavelength*, and is measured in metres. See Figure 12.6.

The wave has also a *frequency*, which is equal to the frequency of the vibrating object. The frequency of the wave is expressed as the number of pressure peaks passing a fixed point per second.

The quantities wavelength (λ, the Greek letter 'lambda' – English 'L') and frequency (f) are related by the equation:

$$\lambda \times f = c$$

where c is the speed of sound in metres per second.

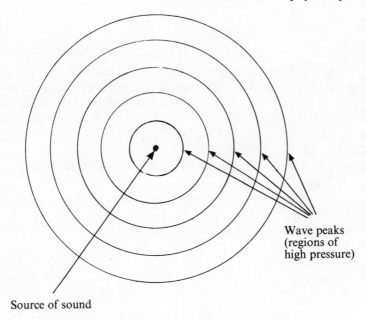

Figure 12.5   How a sound wave propagates from a point source

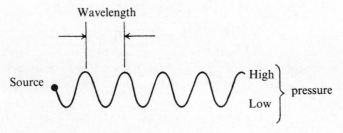

Figure 12.6   The wavelength of a pressure wave

This is another triangular relationship like Ohms law so that the cover up rule applies:

$$\frac{c}{\lambda f}$$

Example: A loudspeaker emits a sound wave at 1 kHz. What is the wavelength of this wave, given that the speed of sound in air is 330 m/s?

Solution: Since $\lambda \times f = c$, $\lambda = \frac{c}{f}$.

Substitute the data for c = 330 m/s, and for f = 1000 Hz.

Then $\lambda = \frac{330}{1000}$ = .33m, or 33 cms.

205

Light

Light, like sound, travels in waves; but the waves are not waves of pressure. Light travels as an electromagnetic wave of variation of electron density of magnetic and electric fields in free space. It is of the same family as radio waves, and travels at the radio speed of 3×10^8 m/s (300 million metres per second).

The definitions of frequency and wavelength apply to light as they do to sound. So does the equation $\lambda \times f = c$, though c has now the very much higher value of 3×10^8 m/s.

Examples: (a) A radio wave has a frequency of 100 MHz. What is its wavelength?

(b) A light ray has a wavelength of 5×10^{-7}m. What is its frequency?

Solutions: (a) Substitute the data in the equation:

$\lambda = c/f$ with $c = 3 \times 10^8$m/s and $f = 100 \times 10^6$.

Then $\lambda = \dfrac{3 \times 10^8}{100 \times 10^6} = \dfrac{3 \times 10^8}{10^8} = 3m$

(b) Again substitute the data in: $f = \dfrac{c}{\lambda}$ so that $f = \dfrac{3 \times 10^8}{5 \times 10^{-7}}$ Hz

Then $f = \dfrac{3}{5} \times 10^{15}$ Hz or 0.6×10^{15} Hz.

This works out as 6×10^{14} Hz, or 600 million MHz.

Different frequencies of light waves correspond to different colours of light, but the frequencies are much too high to be detected by electronic circuits. So television (see Chapter 14) must use other means to reduce a light pattern to a series of signals.

The response of the human eye to this range of wavelengths is shown in Table 12.1 and Figure 12.7.

Light travels in straight lines, casting sharp shadows, a feature that is described as *rectilinear propagation*. See Figure 12.8. (That statement, as a matter of strict fact, is not wholly true, for the microscope can reveal patterns called *diffraction fringes* which are caused by interference with the waves of light. Because the wavelength of light is very short, however – less than one thousandth of a millimetre – these diffraction effects do not show up significantly in most optical equipment.)

The path of a light ray can therefore, for most practical purposes, be represented by a straight line drawn from the light source to whatever surface the light happens to strike. What happens after that depends on the nature of that surface. The light may be absorbed by the surface, so heating it. Or it may be reflected from the surface in another direction. Or it may be transmitted through the material, changing its direction because of the effects of *refraction*.

Table 12.1   The visible section of the electromagnetic spectrum

Colour	Wavelength (nanometres)
Ultra-violet	below 350
Violet	350 to 400
Indigo	400 to 424
Blue	424 to 491
Green	491 50 575
Yellow	575 to 585
Orange	585 to 647
Red	647 to 700
Infra-red	Beyond 700

The visible colours thus lie in the frequency range of about 4.285×10^{14} Hz to 8.57×10^{14} Hz.

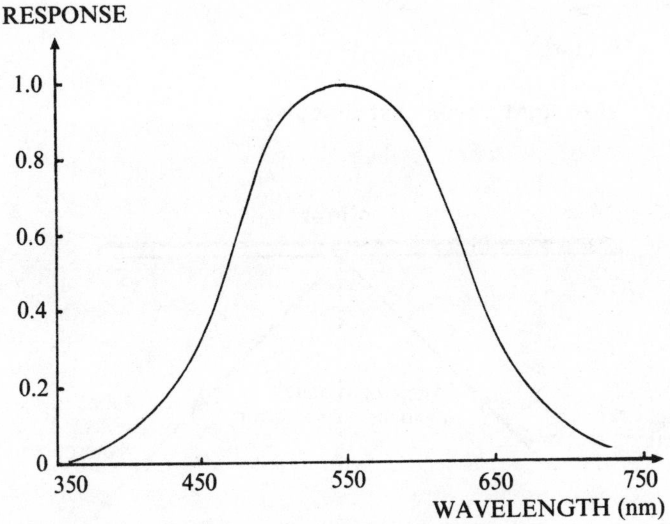

Figure 12.7   Response of human eye to visible light

See Figure 12.10.

When a light ray is reflected from a surface, the angle between the reflected ray and the reflecting surface is equal to the angle between the incoming ray and the same surface. These angles are, by convention, measured from the *normal* – which is a line drawn out at right angles from the surface. See Figure 12.9.

Refraction takes place when a light ray passes from one transparent material to another (such as from air to glass, from air to water, or from water to glass).

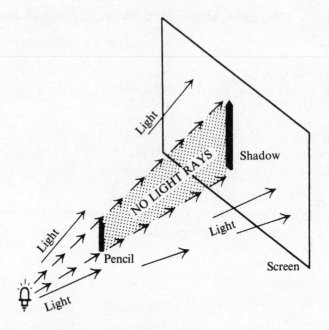

Figure 12.8 How light waves cast shadows

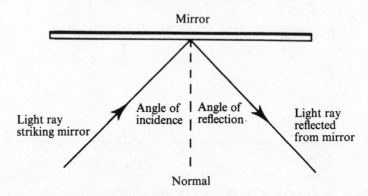

Figure 12.9 How light reflects from a mirror

Refraction is an abrupt change of direction of the light ray at the surface where the transparent materials meet. It is caused by the fact that the speed of light is different when the light is travelling through one type of transparent material than it is when it is travelling through another. Figure 12.10 shows how the ray is bent when passing from the less dense air into the more dense glass.

Lenses are devices which put the principle of the refraction of light to

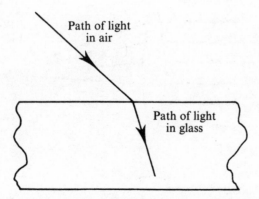

Figure 12.10   The principle of the refraction of a ray of light

important practical uses. A *converging* lens has the property of so changing the directions of parallel rays of light that they converge on to a single point, the *focus*. A *diverging* lens, on the other hand, changes the directions of parallel rays of light so that they spread out on the other side of the lens, appearing there as if they had originated from a focus on the side of the glass on which they first impinge. See Figure 12.11.

Converging lenses are used to create images on screens. These images can be either smaller (*diminished*) or larger (*magnified*) than the objects from which the images are taken.

Colour

The sensation known as colour is the effect on the eye of the impact of light rays of different frequency. The pure white light of the sun is a mixture of all the visible frequencies of light.

These different frequencies can be separated out from white light by the refracting action of a wedge-shaped piece of glass called a *prism*. A prism produces a spectrum of colours, in the following ascending order of light frequency: red, orange, yellow, green, blue, violet (indigo also is sometimes identified as existing between blue and violet). Light frequencies lower than red are called *infra-red*: those higher than violet are called *ultra-violet*. See Figure 12.12.

A reasonably pure white light can be obtained by mixing together in the correct proportions three colours only of the complete spectrum. Such colours are called *primary* colours. The primary colours used in colour TV and some colour photographic processes are red, green and blue. The mixture of these three in the correct proportions gives a good quality of white light.

By appropriate choice of the standard frequencies of the primary colours, a

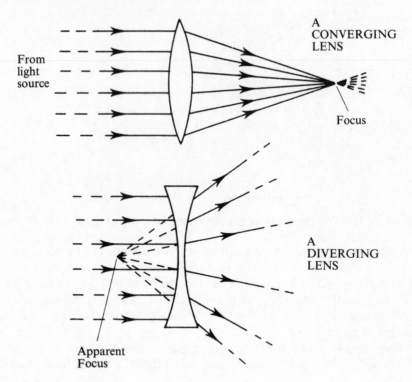

Figure 12.11   Lenses

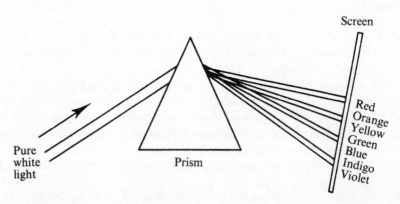

Figure 12.12   How a prism separates out the component colours of white light

wide range of *secondary* colours can be obtained by *mixing*. Some samples of secondary colours obtained in this way are shown in Figure 12.13. It will be seen

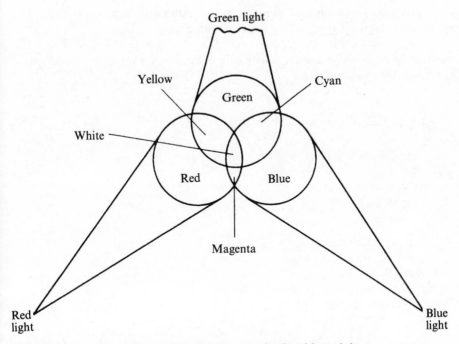

Figure 12.13   How secondary colours are obtained by mixing

that yellow can be obtained from an appropriate combination of red and green, cyan from green and blue, magenta from red and blue – and white from a combination of all three primary colours: red, green and blue.

Secondary colours can be obtained either by adding primary colours together (in what are called *additive* mixers) or by subtracting primary colours from white light (in *subtractive* mixing). Additive mixing is the process used in colour TV; subtractive mixing in most colour photographic purposes.

The two important quantities required to describe a colour exactly are its *hue* and the degree of its *saturation*. Hue is specified by the proportion of the primary colours which are present in the colour, and describes the colour itself. Saturation is a measure of the *amplitude* of that colour. Desaturation of a colour with white light produces pastel shades.

In colour television it is necessary that the hue and the degree of colour saturation of every part of the picture is defined, as well as its brightness (*luminance*) and its exact position in the scene being televised. In the colour TV system, the colour information signal is referred to as 'chrominance'.

Exercise 12.1

Use a suitable colour TV receiver fed with a standard colour bar test signal and note the order of the colour bars. (This is usually, white, yellow, cyan, green, magenta, red, blue and black, reading from left to right.) In turn, switch off the red, blue and green guns, both singly and in pairs and record the colour bar patterns obtained. Compare the findings with Figure 12:13.

Note. It is important to recognize that dangerously high voltages will exist in certain areas of the receiver. Great care should therefore be exercised when carrying out this experiment.

Test questions

12.1   The unit of mass in the SI system of units is the
(a) newton
(b) kilogram
(c) cubic metre
(d) newton metre.

12.2   Heat is transferred through metals by
(a) radiation alone
(b) convection alone
(c) radiation and convection
(d) conduction alone.

12.3   A sound wave of 1 kHz travels through air at approximately 330 m/s, its wavelength is
(a) 33 cm
(b) 300 m
(c) 1 km
(d) 3 km.

12.4   An object held in a light beam casts a shadow because
(a) light reflects, changing direction
(b) light refracts, changing direction
(c) light is focused by a lens
(d) light travels in straight lines.

12.5   When a mechanical force causes movement
(a) temperature is reduced
(b) work is done
(c) mass is increased
(d) energy is destroyed.

12.6   Any colour of light can be obtained by mixing
(a) red, green and blue light
(b) red, blue and cyan light
(c) blue, yellow and green light
(d) green, cyan and magenta light.

13 Binary numbers and logic

Refer to syllabus sections 04(4.5) and 07(005,007)

Ordinary counting is done by means of a system based on ones and tens. Take a random number like 3582. It will help later on to suppose that a decimal point is in position to the immediate right of the digit '2', but it is always left out of a whole number for reasons of convenience.

The same digit '2' represents, by the rules of the *denary system* (as it is called), two units of 'one'. The digit '8' to its left represents eight units of 10. The next digit further left represents five units of 10^2, or 100; and the digit '3' still further left represents three units of 10^3, or 1000.

If the number 3582 had been larger, the same rules would continue to apply, every digit in places further to the left of the (suppressed) decimal point representing the stated number of successively higher powers of 10. Thus 3 872 496, broken down, comes to:

10^6	10^5	10^4	10^3	10^2	10^1	10^0
or	*or*	*or*	*or*	*or*	*or*	*or*
1 000 000	100 000	10 000	1000	100	10	1
×	×	×	×	×	×	×
3	8	7	2	4	9	6

In other words, 3 millions, plus 8 hundreds of thousands, plus 7 tens of thousands, plus 2 thousands, and so on, make up the full number you are

213

seeking to express in denary.

If the number you want contains a fraction which is less than 1, the decimal point ceases to be suppressed and *must* be put in to the right of the digit expressing 'ones'. The first such digit to the right of the decimal point gives the number of 10^{-1}, or one-tenths, you wish to express; the second gives the number of one-hundredths (10^{-2}); the third the number of one-thousandths (10^{-3}); and so on as before with the addition of the minus sign in the number used to express the power.

In systems like the denary, 10 is called the *base*, and the various superscripts applied to it are called *exponents*.

Ten, however, is not the only number which can be used as the base for a system of counting. Bases other than 10 can be used without any change in the method of writing the exponents. In the scale of 8, for example, the number 163 means 3 ones, plus 6 eights, plus one $8^2 (=64)$ – making a total of $64 + 48 + 3 = 115$ in denary terms. Such a scale is used in some computing work, as is a scale of 16. In this latter *hexadecimal* scale, as it is called, difficulties arise in expressing the denary numbers 10, 11, 12, 13, 14 and 15,; and six letters of the alphabet (A, B, C, D, E, and F respectively) are used for the purpose.

Another much-used counting system is the *binary* scale. As its name implies, the base is 2. Powers of 2 again depend on distance to the left of the suppressed decimal, and the only digits used are 0 and 1. Thus the binary number 1101 is the equivalent of a denary number calculated as follows: the first place to the left of the suppressed binary point represents 2^0, or 'ones'. There is a 1 in that place, so it must be counted. The second place to the left of the point represents 2^1, or 'twos'. There is a zero in this place, so nothing is added to the count. The third place represents 2^2, or 4; and a 1 in this position means that 4 must be added to the count – just as a 1 in the fourth place to the left ($2^3 = 8$) means that 8 must be added. The full denary equivalent is thus $1 + 0 + 4 + 8 = 13$.

Binary figures *to the right* of the binary point are used to express binary fractions, such as $\frac{1}{2}, \frac{1}{4}, \frac{1}{8}, \frac{1}{16}, \frac{1}{32}$, and so on to further inverse powers of 2.

Figure 13.1 shows a table of powers applicable to denary and binary systems which it may be convenient to have printed side by side.

Denary numbers are converted to binary numbers by the following process. Divide the denary number by 2, and write down *any remainder* at the head of a separate *remainder column*. Divide what is left by 2, and again write down any remainder in the remainder column, immediately under the first entry. Clearly, all entries in this remainder column must be either 1s (if there is a remainder after a division by 2) or 0s (if there is not).

Continue the process until your original denary number is reduced to 1. 'Two into one doesn't go'; so put in a zero as the last entry in the *diminishing number* column, and the remainder 1 as the last entry in the remainder column. Then read off the remainder column *starting from the bottom and moving upwards*, and

Power	of TEN	of TWO
0	1	1
1	10	2
2	100	4
3	1 000	8
4	10 000	16
5	100 000	32
6	1 000 000	64
7	10 000 000	128
8	100 000 000	256
9	1 000 000 000	512
.	.	.
.	.	.
.	.	.
.	.	.

Figure 13.1 The powers of ten and of two

write down the ensuing string of 0s and 1s, *from left to right*. The left most bit is described as the 'most significant bit' (MSB) and the right most as the 'least significant bit' (LSB).

Example. Convert the denary number 527 to binary.

Solution.

	Diminishing Number	*Remainder*
Divide 527 by 2	263	1
÷2	131	1
÷2	65	1
÷2	32	1
÷2	16	0
÷2	8	0
÷2	4	0
÷2	2	0
÷2	1	0
÷2	0	1

Start from the bottom of the remainder column and write out the digits in it from left to right. The binary number corresponding to denary 527 then appears as: 1000001111.

The conversion of binary numbers to denary is much simpler if the table of powers in Figure 13.1 is properly applied. Write out the binary figure, which we will say is 100101. *Ignore all the zeros in that figure*, and concentrate on the

215

correct power of 2 to attribute to each of the 1s according to its position in the binary number. Thus:

$$\begin{array}{ccccccc}
2^5 & & & 2^2 & & 2^0 \\
| & & & | & & | \\
1 & 0 & 0 & 1 & 0 & 1 \\
| & & & | & & | \\
32 & & & 4 & & 1
\end{array}$$

Then add the denary figures which have emerged from this process, and the full denary equivalent of binary 100101 appears as $32 + 4 + 1 = 37$.

Binary arithmetic

The addition of binary numbers is carried out in the same way as that of denary numbers save that two 1s add to 'zero and 1 carried forward', while three 1s equal '1 and 1 carried forward'. Thus:

$$\begin{array}{r}
1011 \\
\underline{1101} \\
11000
\end{array}$$

In the units column the two 1s add up to binary 10 ('one zero', *not* 'ten'). A zero is written down and 1 is carried forward. The next column then appears as $1 + 1 + 0$, which therefore again means that a zero is written down and 1 is carried forward. The same thing happens in the third column, but in the fourth the carry-forward makes the total $1 + 1 + 1$. So a 1 is now written down, leaving the carry-forward 1 to appear alone in the fifth column.

Binary subtraction can be done by the familiar 'borrow' method used in denary subtraction; but an easier method is available which is called '*2's complement*'. Write down the large number, and below it the smaller number 'complemented'. This means that every 0 in the smaller number becomes a 1, and every 1 a 0. Next, add to this complemented binary number the unit 1, and the result is *added* to the larger number. The figure on the extreme left of the sum so obtained is disregarded, and what is left is the result of the binary subtraction.

Note that both the binary numbers in this method of subtraction must have the same number of digits. If they do not, add the appropriate number of zeros to the left of the smaller number.

Example: Subtract binary 110 from binary 1101.
Solution: Write down the larger figure 1101
Since it has four digits, the smaller number must be rewritten as.....0110
Complement this binary number 1001

Add 1 to the answer and it becomes .... <u>1010</u>
Add, by binary methods, to make..10111
Discard the left-hand digit, and the binary remainder is 0111.

This remainder is the equivalent of denary 7, which is indeed the remainder when binary 110 (= denary 6) is subtracted from binary 1101 (= denary 13).

The fact that the '2's complement' method involves only addition makes it the method favoured in all computing, for the cost of a different set of circuits for subtraction is thereby avoided.

The peculiar advantage of the binary scale in electronic counting systems is that only the figure 0 and 1 need to be represented. It is much easier to design a circuit in which a transistor is biased either fully on or fully off than it is to design one in which varying values of collector voltage represent different figures in the denary scale. Thus a binary system needs no carefully calculated bias voltages, and will not be greatly affected by changes in either supply voltage or component values.

In a normal system of digital logic, '1' is represented by a comparatively high voltage – say 3V, 5V, 10V, 12V or whatever the supply voltage happens to be – and '0' by a much lower voltage – typically around 0 to 0.2V.

Logic gates

A *gate* is a circuit which allows a signal to pass through when it is open but blocks the signal when it is closed. The opening and closing of the gate is done by means of other electrical signals.

A logic gate uses only digital signals of the 0 or 1 type, and the aim of all logic gate circuits is to ensure that the output becomes 1 only when some fixed combination of inputs present themselves to the gate.

The simplest types of gate have two inputs only. They are called AND, OR, NAND and NOR gates according to their action.

The action of a gate is shown in its so-called *truth-table* – a list of the outputs obtained from every possible combination of inputs into it. Such a table is much easier to understand than is the circuit diagram of a gate, which when an IC is used may not even be possible to follow out at all.

The standard actions of the four types of gate mentioned are represented on diagrams by the symbols shown in Figure 13.2. It will be noted that the British Standard (BS) symbols used in all City & Guilds of London Institute examinations differ from the international symbols which will be found in most logic diagrams. Both sets of symbols should be learnt. The international symbols are sometimes described as the 'United States Military Specification.'

The truth tables for all AND, OR, NAND and NOR gates are given in the lower half of Figure 13.2. These show that the output of the AND gate is 1 only

217

SYMBOLS-INTERNATIONAL

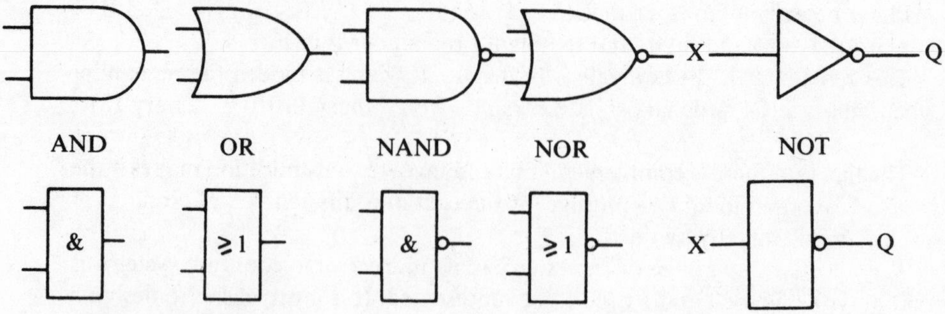

| AND | OR | NAND | NOR | NOT |

BRITISH STANDARD

TRUTH TABLES

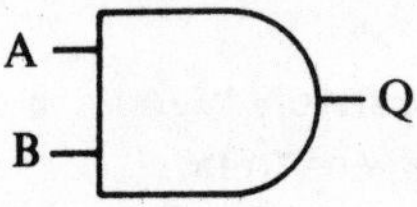

AND

A	B	Q
0	0	0
0	1	0
1	0	0
1	1	1

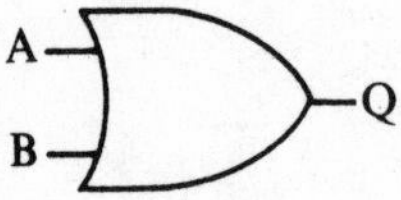

OR

A	B	Q
0	0	0
0	1	1
1	0	1
1	1	1

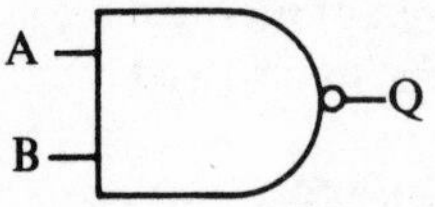

NAND

A	B	Q
0	0	1
0	1	1
1	0	1
1	1	0

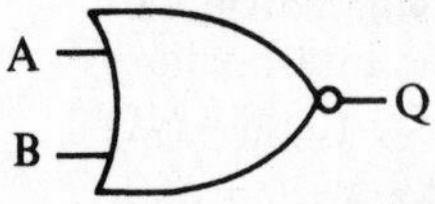

NOR

A	B	Q
0	0	1
0	1	0
1	0	0
1	1	0

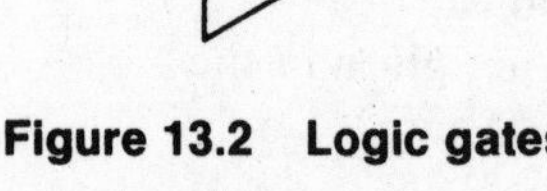

NOT

X	Q
1	0
0	1

Figure 13.2   Logic gates – their symbols and truth tables

when *both* inputs are 1 (i.e., only when both Input A *and* Input B are at logic 1). The output of the OR gate is 1 when *either* Input A *or* Input B is at logic 1.

The NAND and NOR gates are no more than the inverses of the AND and the OR gates respectively. Check carefully through their inputs and outputs in Figure 13.2 to see what this implies.

A fifth type of logic unit often associated with these gates is the *inverter*, or *complementer*, or NOT gate, also shown in Figure 13.2. This gate has a single input and an output which is *invariably the inverse of its input*.

Gate combinations

By suitable connection of the appropriate standard gates, any type of truth table can be achieved. Conversely, since the truth of all the standard gates are known, a truth table for any combination of gates can be worked out. The procedure is as follows:

1. Prepare a series of columns for the logic gate combination whose truth table you wish to work out, and head them A, B, C, etc., for as many original inputs as the combination is to receive.

2. Prepare another set of columns for all the intermediate points in the system where the output of one gate forms the input or inputs to another gate or gates. Label these columns with further consecutive letters of the alphabet – D, E, etc.

3. Label a final column Q, for the final output.

4. Fill in the first set of input columns (A, B and C in the truth table in Figure 13.3 with a series of binary numbers starting with 000, 001, 010, 011 and so on, until the row in which the numbers are all 1s is reached.

5. Then work out and fill in for every D, E, etc., column the output which the intermediate gate in question would give if it received the inputs displayed in columns A, B and C.

6. Complete every row by working out and filling in the final output Q.

Figure 13.3, for example, shows a circuit consisting of two NAND gates followed by a NOR gate. It has three inputs – A, B, C, two intermediate stages – D, E – and an output Q. Six columns are thus needed.

The A, B, C columns are first filled in, with all the binary numbers from 000 to 111 – so providing for every possible combination of inputs. The intermediate values in columns D and E are then entered from the truth table for the NAND gate (which you will remember shows a 0 output *only* if *both* inputs are at 1. Otherwise the output is 1). Finally, the Q column is filled in from the truth table for the NOR gate, given in Figure 13.2.

Note that this particular logic gate gives an output only for the combination of inputs shown. These inputs might represent either (say) the number 7 (binary 111), or a series of signals from safety switches which would permit a machine to be switched on only when certain combinations of switches were pressed.

219

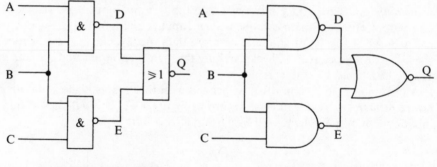

British Standard symbol   International symbol

Truth table

A	B	C	D	E	Q
0	0	0	1	1	0
0	0	1	1	1	0
0	1	0	1	1	0
0	1	1	1	0	0
1	0	0	1	1	0
1	0	1	1	1	0
1	1	0	0	1	0
1	1	1	0	0	1

Figure 13.3   Compiling the truth table for a logic gate combination

Exercise 13.1
The SN7400 integrated circuit contains four NAND gates, each with two inputs, and is available as a 14-pin DIL pack. This can be conveniently mounted on a solderless breadboard for experimental work.

With the IC suitably mounted, connect Pin 14 to the positive terminal of a stabilized 5V supply, and Pin 7 to the negative terminal of the supply. Then connect a voltmeter (using its 10V range) with its positive lead to Pin 3, and its negative to earth. Connect switches between earth and Pins 1 and 2 as shown, labelling the open circuit position '1' and the s/c position '0'. The reason for labelling the switches thus is that closing a switch will result in a very low voltage, so connecting the input to logic zero; while opening the switch will allow the pin to 'float' to +5V, which is logic 1. See Figure 13.4.

Label the switches A and B, and fill in the truth table for the NAND gate.

Note that only certain types of logic gates will 'float' to +5V in this way – normally each input should be taken to either +5V or 0V, and never allowed to float.

Exercise 13.2
Having completed Exercise 1, work out truth tables for the other connections of gates shown, with pin numbers, in Figure 13.5.

Correct tables for these five gate connections are given in Figure 13.9 at the

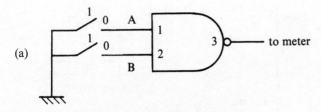

Figure 13.4   Diagram for Exercise 13.1

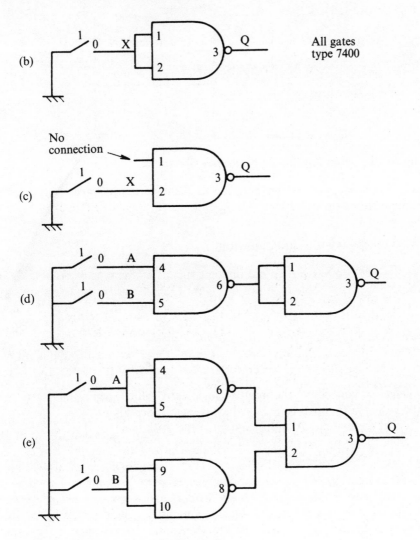

All gates
type 7400

Figure 13.5   Diagram for Exercise 13.2

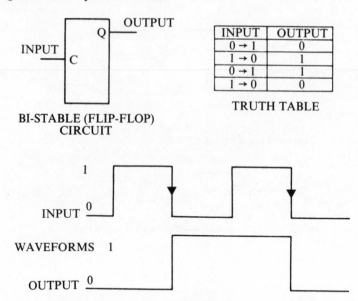

INPUT	OUTPUT
$0 \rightarrow 1$	0
$1 \rightarrow 0$	1
$0 \rightarrow 1$	1
$1 \rightarrow 0$	0

TRUTH TABLE

BI-STABLE (FLIP-FLOP)
CIRCUIT

Figure 13.6   The flip-flop as frequency divider

end of this chapter; but do not consult them until you have really tried to compile your own.

Frequency division and counting

Frequency division is carried out on logic signals by the type of bistable circuit whose basic truth table is shown in Figure 13.6. As the truth table shows, the output only moves from 0 to 1 at every *second* 1-to-0 movement at the input. Thus if the input to such a circuit is a square wave, the output will be a square wave recurring *at half the frequency of the input*.

The output of such a divider stage can of course be taken to the input of a second similar stage so as to achieve another halving of frequency. In this way any given frequency can be divided down by any power of two.

If the input to a chain of divider circuits such as that described is a train of pulses with the number of pulses controlled by a gate, the divider chain will also act as a *counter*. After a number of pulses have been received at the input, the output of every bistable in the chain will be at either 0 or 1, representing a binary digit. Because every divider divides by 2, every output digit represents *a power of 2*, so that the outputs form a binary number equal to the number of input pulses received. Used in this way, the binary divider chain becomes a *binary counter*.

The most common form of binary counter circuit is the so-called BCD (binary-coded decimal) counter, generally encountered nowadays in the form of a single IC. See Figure 13.7. Input pulses up to denary 9 are counted, and binary

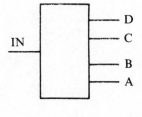

Input pulse no.	D	C	B	A
0	0	0	0	0
1	0	0	0	1
2	0	0	1	0
3	0	0	1	1
4	0	1	0	0
5	0	1	0	1
6	0	1	1	0
7	0	1	1	1
8	1	0	0	0
9	1	0	0	1
10	0	0	0	0

Figure 13.7   A BCD counter and its truth table

outputs can be obtained for four outputs (2^3, 2^2, 2^1, 2^0). On the tenth pulse, all the outputs reset to zero, and an output pulse becomes available to carry over to a second counter stage (2^7, 2^6, 2^5, 2^4) if such is needed.

The outputs from counters such as the BCD can be displayed as decimal figures on seven-segment readouts. A decoder circuit is needed (consisting of logic gates) to ensure that a given binary set of outputs produces the correct decimal number on the readout. The decoder is usually an integrated circuit; and IC chips forming combined counter-decoders, and even counter-decoder-displays, are nowadays available.

By way of illustration of digital techniques, Figure 13.8 shows the block diagram of a simple digital clock. The crystal oscillator runs at a high frequency, at a number of Hz which must be an exact power of 2. The divider chain then divides this frequency down to one pulse per second, one pulse per minute and one pulse per hour. At every divider stage, decoders convert the BCD numbers representing hours, minutes and seconds into voltages which operate the correct segments of a six-figure set of seven-segment displays.

Note that in the 'Hours' display the first figure must always be either a 1 or a blank, so only one line from the decoder is needed for it.

If a gate were to be inserted between the oscillator and the first divider, with a reset so that all the displays could be set to zero, the block diagram of Figure 13.8 would be converted into that of a stop-watch.

Test questions

13.1   If the binary numbers 1001 and 1010 are added, what will the answer be in denary (decimal) notation?
(a) 19
(b) 18

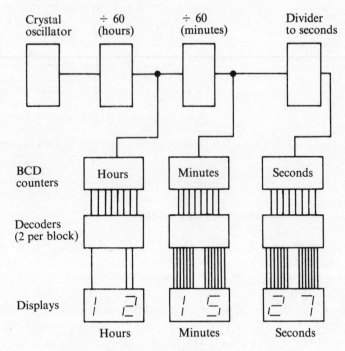

Figure 13.8   Block diagram of a digital clock

Solutions to exercise problems (Figure 13.9)

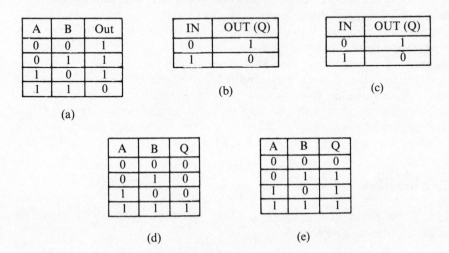

A	B	Out
0	0	1
0	1	1
1	0	1
1	1	0

(a)

IN	OUT (Q)
0	1
1	0

(b)

IN	OUT (Q)
0	1
1	0

(c)

A	B	Q
0	0	0
0	1	0
1	0	0
1	1	1

(d)

A	B	Q
0	0	0
0	1	1
1	0	1
1	1	1

(e)

Figure 13.9   Correct truth tables for Exercises 13.1 and 13.2

(c) 11

(d) 10.

13.2 Which of the following binary codes represents the decimal number 13?

(a) 1110

(b) 0101

(c) 0111

(d) 1101.

13.3 Which of the following binary codes will result in a logic 0 output from a 3 input NAND gate?

(a) 111

(b) 000

(c) 101

(d) 010.

13.4 Adding three binary 1 digits produces the result of

(a) 1 carry 0

(b) 1 carry 1

(c) 3 carry 0

(d) 2 carry 1.

13.5 The 2's complement of 1101 is

(a) 1101

(b) 1011

(c) 0011

(d) 1100.

13.6 After the application of 15 input pulses to a counter constructed from 4 bi-stables, the output will be

(a) 0000

(b) 0111

(c) 1110

(d) 1111.

14 Miscellaneous electronic components and systems

Refer to syllabus sections 04(4.5) and 07(005,007,009)

The tape recorder

The magnetic principles on which the tape recorder works were outlined in Chapter 11. A tape head consists of a ring of soft magnetic material, such as Permalloy, with a very small gap cut into the ring. The ring has a coil wound round it, well away from the gap, and the tape is made to travel a path which feeds it slowly past the gap.

When an electric current is caused to flow through the coil, a large magnetic flux is created inside the soft magnetic material. Some of this flux emerges at the gap (see Figure 14.1). The material used as a coating on the tape is magnetized by this flux as it passes across the gap; and because it is a 'hard' magnetic material, it retains this magnetism and a permanently magnetized section of tape is produced.

To record signals, therefore, the signal current is passed through the coil of the recording head while the tape is caused to move past the gap. The magnetism which represents different parts of the signal wave is thus received and retained by consecutive segments of the moving tape.

Because the transfer characteristic of the magnetic tape is non-linear in the manner shown in Figure 14.2, a bias signal at about 80 kHz upwards, is added to the audio. The effect of this, providing that the bias amplitude is correct, is to transfer the envelope of the total magnetizing current on to the two linear

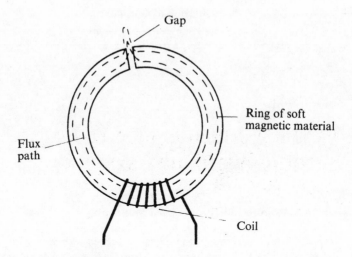

Figure 14.1   A tape-recording head

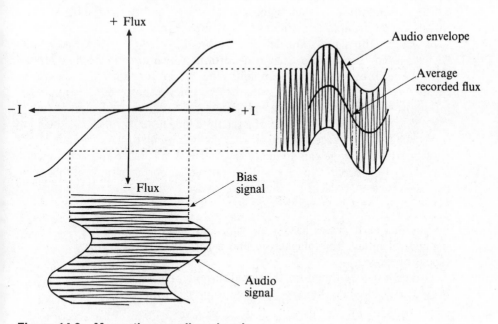

Figure 14.2   Magnetic recording signals

regions as depicted. Figure 14.2 also shows the recorded magnetic flux pattern, the average value of which produces the audio signal on replay with relatively little distortion.

227

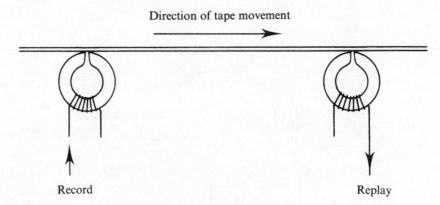

Figure 14.3 **The principle of record and replay**

To replay a recorded tape, the tape is moved, *at the same speed as when it was recording*, past a head of similar construction. (Indeed, a common head for both recording and replay is often used.) The changes in magnetic flux from the tape as it moves past the gap induce a corresponding magnetic flux in the head, which in turn induces voltage signals in the coil wound round the head. These signals are then amplified in the usual way. See Figure 14.3.

In practice, the signals are deliberately pre-distorted, both on *Record* and *Replay*, to compensate for certain distortions which arise in both processes. Both the recording and replay amplifiers therefore incorporate CR (capacitor-resistor) networks capable of varying the frequency response of the amplifiers – HF boost on record, LF boost on playback.

Erasure is effected with the aid of a separate tape head to which is fed a high-frequency signal of large amplitude from the bias oscillator. As the tape moves past the relatively large gap on the *Erase* head, it is magnetized in each direction alternately by succeeding cycles of the *Erase* signal. The amplitude of this signal decreases cycle by cycle as the tape moves away from the centre of the gap, and the action eventually leaves the tape completely de-magnetized.

Recorders of lower quality erase by means of a flow of d.c. to the *Erase* head, or even by the use of a permanent magnet. Although this method provides good erasure, it leaves behind a rather large noise signal on the tape itself.

In most tape recorder designs, the *Record* and *Playback* amplifiers make use of the same amplifying stages, with only the frequency corrections networks being interchanged by switching. Several lower-priced designs also make the loudspeaker power output stage serve as the bias oscillator during recording.

The common record/replay head

Most modern cassette recorders combine their *Record* and *Playback* heads in a single unit. This is possible because both have essentially similar properties and

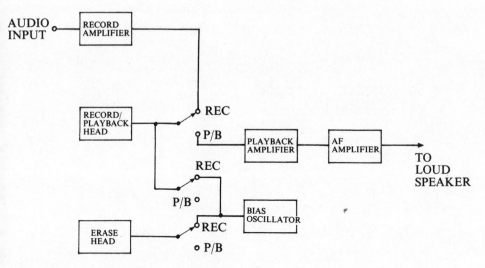

Figure 14.4   A tape recorder system

characteristics.

The combination naturally introduces further problems of *Record/Playback* switching. A block diagram showing how this is achieved is given in Figure 14.4.

The cathode ray tube and the oscilloscope

A cathode ray tube is a transducer which can display three sets of information simultaneously, by using X and Y planes together with brightness variation.

The electron gun of a cathode ray tube (see Figure 14.5) projects a stream of electrons towards the screen, where a spot of light is produced on a phosphor screen. The brightness of this spot depends on the voltage applied to the modulation electrode (which can be either the grid or the cathode of the gun).

The spot of light can be made to move either sideways or up-and-down by so-called *shift voltages*. The X-shift voltage causes the spot to move across the screen horizontally. The Y-shift voltage causes it to move up-and-down the screen vertically.

A cathode ray tube used in television (Figure 14.6) employs all three voltages – X, Y and brightness. The CRT in an oscilloscope uses only the X and Y signals for most purposes.

The block diagram of a simple oscilloscope, omitting both power supplies and brightness controls, is shown in Figure 14.7. A signal applied to the Y-input is attenuated by a calibrated variable attenuator (usually a switch rather than a potentiometer) before being applied to the Y-amplifier. The amplified output

229

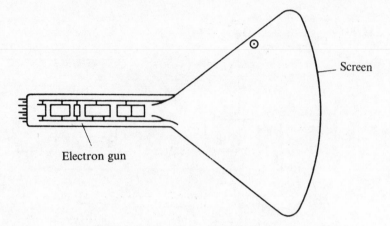

Figure 14.5 A cathode ray tube for use in an oscilloscope

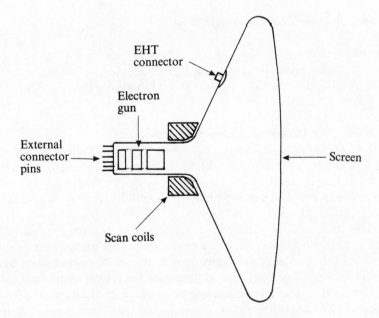

Figure 14.6 A cathode ray tube for use in a TV receiver

drives the Y-plates, which cause the spot to be deflected in the vertical direction. The gain of the amplifier and the settings of the attenuator are matched to the sensitivity of the CRT, and the attenuator is consequently calibrated in volts/cms.

Some of the Y-input signal is fed to a synchronizing circuit which generates a

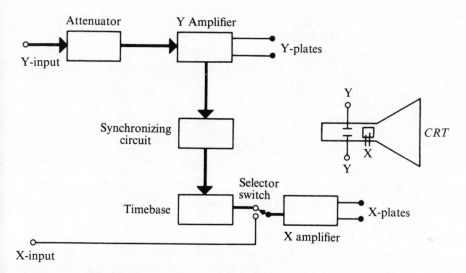

Figure 14.7   The oscilloscope – block diagram

pulse at every signal peak (either positive or negative peaks, usually selected by a switch). Each of these synchronizing pulses is then used to start a *timebase*, a sawtooth signal which is applied via the X-amplifier to the X-plates.

The effect of such a sawtooth waveform is to deflect the electron beam – and so the spot – at a steady speed across the screen in what is called a *sweep*, and then to return it very rapidly indeed to its starting point in what is called *flyback*.

The speed of the timebase sweep can be controlled by a calibrated switch, so that the time needed for the spot to scan every centimetre of the screen can be printed on the switch plate.

Another switch enables the X-amplifier to be used to handle other signals, if desired.

When the CRT is in use, a signal of unknown frequency and amplitude is applied to the Y-input. The Y-attenuator and the timebase speed controls should then be adjusted until a steady display of measurable size appears on the screen. The peak-to-peak amplitude of the waveform is then found by measuring, with the aid of the calibration of the attenuator, the vertical distance between peaks on the graticule. This is a transparent calibrated sheet covering the screen.

The time-period of one cycle is measured on the same graticule, using this time the calibration of the timebase. The frequency of the signal can then be calculated by the formula:

$$\text{Frequency} = \frac{1}{\text{Time period}}$$

231

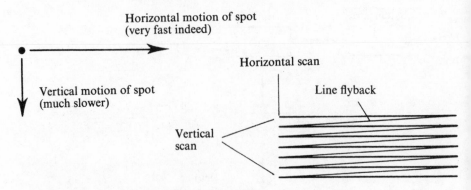

Figure 14.8   The principle of TV scanning

Exercise 14.1
Connect the output of an audio signal generator directly to the Y-input of an oscilloscope. For a range of suitable amplitude and frequency inputs, note that the peak-to-peak amplitude of the signal is the product of height of the trace in centimetres and the setting of the Y-input attenuator. In a similar way, the periodic time is the product of 1 screen wavelength (again in centimetres) and the time-base speed setting. The frequency of each signal can then be found as described above.

Further details of the CRO and of its many applications, with off-screen photographs, can be obtained from the book *Oscilloscopes* by Ian Hickman (Heinemann–Newnes).

Scanning by a television camera

Scanning is a method of obtaining a signal at a fixed repetition frequency from a light-pattern or picture.

A TV camera tube produces at its output a signal which is proportional to the brightness of the light reaching the front surface of the camera tube from every part of the scene being televised. The tube contains an electron beam which is focused to a spot. The position of this spot on the front surface of the tube is the point at which the brightness is sampled to produce an output signal.

In order to produce signals from all parts of the front surface of the tube – and therefore, indirectly, from all parts of the scene – the spot is moved in such a way that it samples all of the tube surface. This is effected by causing the spot to move horizontally, at very high speed, across the face of the tube, and at the same time to move down the tube face from top to bottom – but at a much lower speed. These combined motions constitute *scanning* (see Figure 14.8).

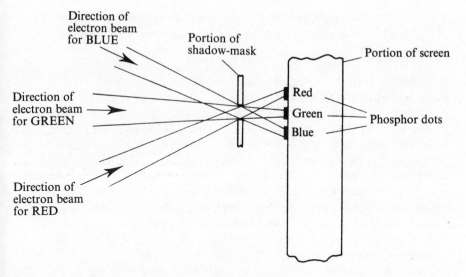

Figure 14.9 How a colour TV receiver tube works

The signal output from the camera tube becomes a d.c. signal of varying amplitudes that represents the brightness of every single tiny area of the tube face as it is scanned by the spot. The signal contains two main frequencies – the horizontal, or *line scanning frequency* and the vertical, or field scanning frequency.

A colour TV tube works on the principle of *additive mixing* of colours, the different colours red, green and blue being projected on to the screen by three electron guns. A shadow-mask fixed close to the screen is pierced by a pattern of holes or slits which prevent the beam from one gun from striking more than one of the three appropriately-coloured phosphor dots in each group of dots on the screen. Thus the beam from one gun lights only the red dots, the beam of the second gun lights only the blue dots and the beam of the third gun lights only the green dots. The sets of dots are so small that the picture looks continuous when scanned by the fast-moving beam, and when viewed from a reasonable distance from the screen.

Every detail of a colour picture can therefore be reproduced by the beams from the three guns, using voltages at the cathodes of the gun which are in the correct proportions to give the brightness and colour required (see Figure 14.9).

A simplified block diagram of a colour TV receiver is shown in Figure 14.10 on page 235.

The modulated carrier signal, which is at a frequency in the range 400–900 MHz, is picked up by the aerial and linked to the *tuner* unit by cable. In the tuner, the required frequency band (which will be about 5.5 MHz wide) is selected and mixed with a sine-wave generated by an oscillator. This *mixer* action produces an intermediate-frequency signal occupying a frequency band of 33.5 – 39.5 MHz. This IF signal is then amplified in the *IF amplifier*.

The AFC (*automatic frequency control*) circuit obtains a d.c. signal from the IF signal, and this d.c. signal is fed back to correct the frequency of the oscillator in the event of *frequency drift*. The use of AFC enables a station to be tuned in, and thereafter to remain correctly tuned. This is essential when tuning of the set is affected by push-button, for all the advantages of push-button tuning would be lost if it were necessary to adjust the tuning of the receiver every time a different station was selected.

In addition, correct reception of colour signals is critically dependent on correct tuning to the signal carrier. AFC would therefore be essential to a colour receiver even if push-button tuning were not used.

The signal from the i.f. amplifier is then passed to a *vision demodulator*. The black-and-white *luminance signal*, which forms the shape and grey tones of the picture, has been amplitude-modulated on to the carrier, and can therefore be recovered by a simple amplitude demodulator in the receiver.

The *sound signal* has been frequency-modulated on to a carrier separated by 6 MHz from the vision carrier. Because of the frequency modulation of the sound signal, it cannot be demodulated by the amplitude demodulator; but a mixing action does nevertheless take place which produces a frequency-modulated 6MHz signal called the *intercarrier* signal. This signal is amplified by the intercarrier amplifier, and then frequency-demodulated to produce the audio-frequency (AF) sound signal which is amplified and applied to the loudspeaker.

To return to the vision demodulator, the vision signal at this point consists of the *luminance signal*, a waveform whose shape depends on the picture information but which has a repetition rate of 15.625 kHz and a wide bandwidth, together with a *modulated sub-carrier* at about 4.43 MHz. The luminance signal, a typical section of which is shown in Figure 14.11, is the signal which carries information about shape and shade, while the modulated sub-carrier at 4.43 MHz carries information about colour. The *luminance amplifier* increases the amplitude of these waveforms for the next stage.

Part of the luminance amplifier signal is taken to the *sync separator* in which the recurring synchronizing pulses (see Figure 14.11) are separated from the luminance signal and also from one another. The *field sync pulse* which recurs at a rate of 50 per second, is used to synchronize the field timebase. This drives the field scan coils and so deflects the CRT spots vertically from top to bottom of the screen face.

The *line sync pulse* is used to synchronize the line timebase. It runs at 15.625 kHz, and drives the line scan coils which deflect the spots across the screen to form lines. The action of this timebase produces a pulse of high voltage which is stepped up still further by a transformer, and then rectified to produce the high EHT (extra high tension) voltage which is needed to accelerate the electron beam towards the screen of the tube.

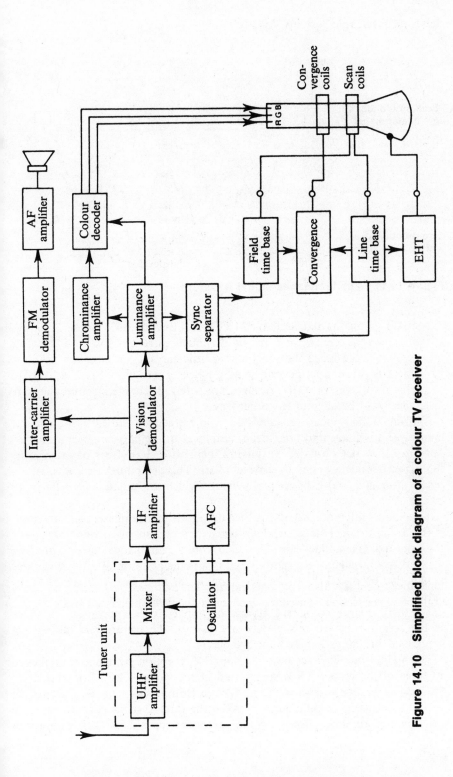

Figure 14.10　Simplified block diagram of a colour TV receiver

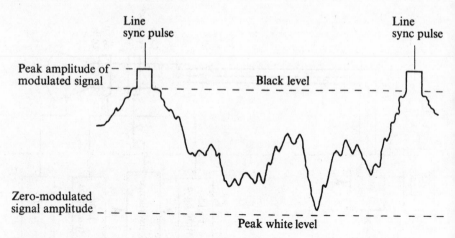

Figure 14.11   The luminance signal waveform

An EHT voltage as high as about 24 kV is required for this purpose. *A voltage of that value is dangerous, and can kill* if enough current is able to flow. Most receivers are so designed that only a very little current can be taken from the EHT circuits. Care must nevertheless be taken to see that all points likely to carry high voltages in a TV receiver are safely discharged before they are disconnected or handled in any other way.

The 4.43 MHz subcarrier signals are also extracted at an early stage in the luminance amplifier, and are further amplified in the chrominance amplifier. They are then demodulated by mixing them with sine waves of exactly the subcarrier frequency and in the correct phase. This demodulation (called *synchronous demodulation*) produces two signals which are called *colour-difference signals*.

The colour-difference signals are then mixed with the luminance signal in part of the colour decoder stage, in which signals representing two of the three basic colours – red, green, blue – are subtracted from the luminance signal to produce the third colour signal. Remember that it was the addition of all three colour signals that produced the luminance signal in the first place back at the transmitter.

The three separate colour signals are now applied to the appropriate cathodes of the colour tube. In this way, every part of the picture has the correct luminance (brightness) and colour balance.

The highly-simplified account of colour TV reception given above applies to all three of the colour TV systems used in the world – NTSC in the USA, SECAM in France and Russia, and PAL in Britain, Germany and the rest of Western Europe. The differences between the three systems concern only the chrominance amplifier and the colour decoder blocks (see block diagram in

Figure 14.10), but the differences within these blocks are great.

NTSC is the simplest system, since it dates from 1951; PAL the most complex. Details of the differences are of interest only to the specialist. They are covered in the more specialized Sections of the syllabus for Part 3 of the City and Guilds course in electronics for the service engineer.

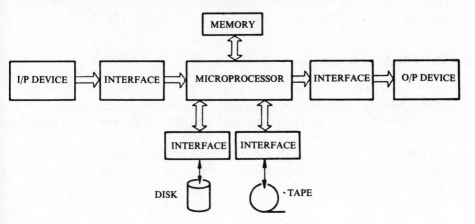

Figure 14.12   The basic computer: a block diagram

The basic digital computer system

A block diagram of the digital computer is shown in Figure 14.12. The basic functions are: INPUT – PROCESSING STAGES – OUTPUT, with the various processing stages being controlled by *programs* held in the computer's *memory*.

The *input* device reads data reaching it from outside sources and converts these data into a form capable of being understood by the computer. Input devices include *keyboards, punched cards or paper tape, magnetic tape or disks*, and even analogue transducers such as *level detectors* and *sensors* of heat and light. These data may either be fed into the input device over a period of time, or may appear there almost immediately before use.

Should the input device be unable to generate a correct code or signal level, it is the function of an *interface* to match these parameters to the requirements of the computer.

The memory

In addition to the program that controls the way in which the computer operates, the memory has to hold or store the data items that are waiting to be processed. This requires two types of memory device. One that will retain its information even when the power is switched off, is called a read only memory or ROM and carries the operating instructions. The second which has to be capable of being written to and read from almost in a random manner is therefore known as a random access memory or RAM. Because of its retentive memory, the ROM is described as being *non-volatile*, while the RAM which loses the data when the power is switched off is said to be *volatile*.

The disk-tape units

These devices act as an extension or back-up to the working of the computer's internal memory. During normal working, the computer may need to perform a variety of tasks, each requiring a different program. These *service programs*, as they are called, are conveniently stored on magnetic tape or disk.

Tape or disk units are also valuable for storing masses of data of the type that might be gathered during such applications as *process control* or *quality control*. Since both these forms of back-up devices handle binary data in a way that is not normally acceptable to the computer as it stands, they also need interfacing in the same way as did the input.

The microprocessor

This block contains three important sections:

- A *control* section to generate all the necessary timing functions.
- An *arithmetic and logic* unit to carry out the required calculations in either binary arithmetic or binary logic form.
- An *accumulator* to hold the results of any operation before it becomes convenient to pass them to the memory, either for storage or for output.

Keyboard

A keyboard is constructed from a matrix of input and output lines, with the required interconnections being provided by suitably positioned diodes. A section of such a structure is shown in Figure 14.13. Before a key is pressed, each output bit line b_6 to b_0 is held at 0 volts or logic 0 by the action of the load resistors. When a key is pressed, $+5$ volts is applied to the appropriate input line so that any diodes connected to it become forward biased and the corresponding output bit line is pulled up to $+5$ volts or logic 1. Some keyboards produce an output coded in ACSII (American Standard Code for Information Interchange) and Figure 14.13 shows the pattern of diodes for the upper case letters, A = 1000001, B = 1000010, C = 1000011, D = 1000100, with the most

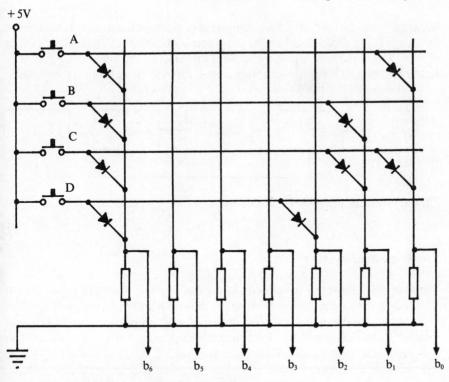

Figure 14.13   Section of keyboard matrix

significant bit (MSB) on the left and the least significant bit (LSB) on the right. Operation of the keyboard *shift key* causes bit five (b_5) to be changed from 0 to 1 to produce the lower case set of characters.

Output devices

Output devices form the computer's contact with the outside world over which it is attempting to exert some form of control. They include such devices as *card* or *tape punching machines, visual display units, printers,* and even such analogue devices as *motors, loudspeakers* or *lights.*

An *interface* between the microprocessor and the various output devices is again needed to match the signal output from the computer to the signal input required by the relevant output device.

Hardware, software and firmware

These are jargon terms much used in computing. Hardware is used to describe the physical devices such as disk drives, printers, computers and even the integrated circuits from which a computer is constructed. Software is simply the physically intangible items like the programs without which the system cannot operate. Often the software programs are stored in a hardware device such as a ROM or a disk. This composite item is then referred to as firmware.

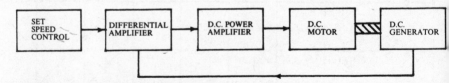

Figure 14.14   A speed control system

Speed control system

The essential features of the closed loop control system shown in Figure 14.14, are the differential amplifier described in Chapter 8 and the d.c. generator. The latter is a device that generates a d.c. output voltage proportional to the speed of rotation and this is driven by direct coupling to the load driving d.c. motor. The d.c. generator or *tachogenerator* thus produces a d.c. voltage level that is indicative of the speed of the motor. The *Set speed* control sets a nominal d.c. level for input to the differential amplifier which compares this with the output from the tachogenerator. If the amplifier detects that the motor is running slow, then it generates an increased level of output voltage, that when amplified by the d.c. power amplifier causes the motor to increase speed. This sequence of events is reversed if the load on the motor decreases.

Test questions

14.1   The UK UHF colour TV system uses
(a) SECAM
(b) MAC
(c) PAL
(d) NTSC.

14.2   A digital computer uses an interface circuit
(a) for exchanging signals between devices
(b) for arithmetic calculations
(c) to control the processing of data
(d) as an analogue transducer.

14.3   The gap in the record head of a tape recorder

(a) is for the tape to pass through
(b) allow for expansion of the metal
(c) must be large
(d) is where the magnetic flux affects the tape

14.4   An oscilloscope cathode ray tube needs
(a) a flat surface on which measurements can be made
(b) a large amplitude square wave for deflection
(c) a large spot size for accurate measurements
(d) beam deflection using coils and magnets.

14.5   The Y amplifier of an oscilloscope has a sensitivity of 50 mV/cm. What is the peak to peak voltage of the displayed waveform if the total deflection is 5 cm?
(a) 500 mV
(b) 250 mV
(c) 55 mV
(d) 10 mV.

14.6   The luminance signal in a colour TV receiver carries
(a) black and white picture information
(b) synchronizing information
(c) sound information
(d) colour information.

Appendix 1 Answers to test questions

Chapter 2	2.1(b),	2.2(c),	2.3(b),	2.4(a),	2.5(c),	2.6(d).
Chapter 3	3.1(b),	3.2(c),	3.3(d),	3.4(a),	3.5(d),	3.6(d).
Chapter 4	4.1(c),	4.2(a),	4.3(b),	4.4(b),	4.5(d),	4.6(b).
Chapter 5	5.1(a),	5.2(d),	5.3(b),	5.4(c),	5.5(c),	5.6(d).
Chapter 6	6.1(a),	6.2(c),	6.3(b),	6.4(d),	6.5(d),	6.6(c).
Chapter 7	7.1(b),	7.2(d),	7.3(d),	7.4(a),	7.5(a),	7.6(c).
Chapter 8	8.1(a),	8.2(d),	8.3(c),	8.4(a),	8.5(c),	8.6(c).
Chapter 9	9.1(b),	9.2(d),	9.3(c),	9.4(a),	9.5(c),	9.6(c).
Chapter 10	10.1(d),	10.2(d),	10.3(c),	10.4(b),	10.5(d),	10.6(a).
Chapter 11	11.1(c),	11.2(b),	11.3(c),	11.4(a),	11.5(a),	11.6(c).
Chapter 12	12.1(b),	12.2(d),	12.3(a),	12.4(d),	12.5(b),	12.6(a).
Chapter 13	31.1(a),	13.2(d)	13.3(a),	13.4(b),	13.5(c),	13.6(d).
Chapter 14	14.1(c),	14.2(a),	14.3(d),	14.4(a),	14.5(b),	14.6(a).

Appendix 2 Examination structure and assessments

224–1–01 Electronics systems (multiple choice paper).
224–1–02 In-course assignments (locally assessed).
224–1–03 EEB Practical test (externally assessed).

Appendix 3 The Part 1 EEB
Practical Test

Section A (10 minutes). This is a tool identification exercise. The candidate has to list a number of tools that will be required to carry out the exercise in section B. The problem here usually revolves around the soldering iron, stand, solder etc. The candidate should be encouraged to consider that these items form a solder station and hence can be listed as a single tool only. The tool list typically consists of solder station, desoldering tools, track cutters, wire cutters and circuit board clamp or holder.

Section B (45 minutes). This part of the test typically involves removing one IC from a part of the circuit board and fitting another in a different position. The removed IC is expected to appear to be in good condition in spite of the removal. The test further requires the candidate to solder in position a number of resistors or similar components and to repair a broken track.

Section C (45 minutes). This is a test to exercise the candidates' ability to use both a multi-range meter and oscilloscope to obtain static and dynamic voltage levels in a working circuit and to sketch the various waveforms present. It is therefore important that the candidate should be able to interpret time and voltage measurements as well as the time/frequency relationship.

Appendix 4 Part 1 Syllabus

This abridged version of the Part 1 syllabus is intended to be used as an index guide to the contents of the various chapters. For precise details, the reader is referred to the full City and Guilds of London Institute Part 1 syllabus.

01   Study of the electronics industry (**Chapter 1**).
1.1 to 1.4   Organization of industry.
1.5 to 1.6   Electronics and the community.

02   Health and safety practices (**Chapter 2**).
2.1 to 2.8   Implementation and application of the Health and Safety Act within the work place.

03   Marking out, cutting and connecting electronic assemblies (**Chapter 5**).
3.1 to 3.2   The selection, care and maintenance of hand tools.

07   Section 008   Heat and mechanical units.

04   Interpreting system block diagrams by function and waveforms (**Chapters 7, 8, 9, 13 and 14**).
4.1 to 4.2   Study of listed standard systems. AM and FM transmitters and receivers, cathode ray oscilloscope, speed control, phase locked loop, computer system, colour TV receiver, digital clock, tape recorder, power supply.
4.3 to 4.4   Study of the methods and typical devices used to control and display signals input to, and output from, each of the listed systems.
4.5 to 4.8   Study of the characteristics, typical waveforms and applications of

amplifiers, oscillators, modulators/demodulators, filters, power supplies, waveshaping and logic devices.

07　Sections 005, 006, 009, 010　Waveforms, transmission, light, sound.

05　Circuit construction (**Chapter 5**).

5.1 to 5.4　Identification, selection and use of components by characteristics and function. Assembly and repair of circuit boards.

07　Sections 001, 002, 003, 004, 007. Primary and secondary cells. Circuits, resistance and electrical units. Basic magnetism. Capacitance. Calculations.

06　Use of power sources, signal sources and measuring instruments (**Chapters 4 and 10**).

6.1 to 6.6　The selection of suitable power and signal sources to test components and systems. Limitations of various measuring devices relative to loading and waveshape. Tests for serviceability of components and systems.

6.6 to 6.9　Measurement of characteristics and the graphical display of same. Calculations associated with bandwidth of amplifiers. Calculations or resistive networks. Recording graphical and tabular results from experimental data. Formulation of conclusions.

07　Sections 001, 002, 005, 006, 007. Primary and secondary cells. Circuits, resistance and electrical units. Waveforms. Transmission. Calculations.

0.7　Science background (**Chapters 3 to 14**).
　　001 Primary and secondary cells (**Chapter 10**)
　　002 Circuits, resistance and electrical units (**Chapters 5 and 10**)
　　003 Basic magnetism (**Chapter 11**)
　　004 Capacitance (**Chapter 6**)
　　005 Waveforms (**Chapters 8, 9, 10, 13 and 14**)
　　006 Transmission (**Chapter 9**)
　　007 Calculations (**Chapters 3 to 14**)
　　008 Heat and mechanical units (**Chapter 12**)
　　009 Light (**Chapters 12 and 14**)
　　010 Sound (**Chapter 12**)

Appendix 5 Multiple-choice examination questions: guidance to examination candidates

The examining bodies for electronics servicing rely considerably on the use of multiple-choice questions at all levels, and the lower levels are examined totally by this means. The sheer size of a multiple-choice paper often leads candidates into feeling that time is short, leading to a feeling of urgency which results in bad or even silly choices being made. The first point to understand, then, is that the time allocation is in fact quite generous, and the size of the paper is due to the space that is needed for printing diagrams and for the choices of answers.

The golden rule for answering any multiple-choice question is to *formulate your own answer to the question* before looking at the choice of answers, and then selecting the answer that most closely fits with your own. In this way, when you know the answer as you read the question you will not be distracted by reading over the list of answers, all but one of which *will be designed to distract you*. On your first reading of a paper, answer all of the questions that you can using this method, and only then proceed to look at the others.

If you are unsure of an answer of your own, then you can usually reject all but two of the possible answers that are provided. If you are genuinely uncertain about the correct choice of these two, then you can opt for one or the other knowing that your chances of being correct are considerably higher than they would have been if you had guessed or written down an answer letter or number at random.

A methodical approach like this can considerably improve any candidate's score in a multiple-choice examination, particularly in City and Guilds papers where each question is accompanied by two or more answers which are obviously incorrect even if your knowledge of the subject is not as detailed as it ought to be.

Index